TEILHARD DE CHARDIN:
SCIENTIST AND SEER

CHARLES E. RAVEN

TEILHARD
DE CHARDIN
SCIENTIST
AND SEER

HARPER & ROW, PUBLISHERS
New York and Evanston

LIBRARY OF CONGRESS CATALOG CARD NUMBER: 63-7982

Preface

NOW THAT *Le Figaro* has told us that the five volumes of Teilhard's work published in France since his death on Easter Day 1955 have sold some three hundred thousand copies, and that despite their difficulty competent scholars on the continent regard him as the greatest philosopher of our time, it is obviously important that some account of his life and thought and of his special significance for English readers should be made available. I had hoped that one of his personal friends in London or Cambridge would give us a lead, and that younger students of scientific and international problems would follow it up with detailed accounts. A contemporary of his like myself, especially one who is neither a palaeontologist nor a Roman Catholic, cannot hope to do justice to the subject. I must apologise in advance for the attempt.

When five years ago my wife's friends in Belgium and Paris commended him to us, I realised how completely his interpretation of the evolutionary process fulfilled the hopes which Dr. William Temple discussed with me at our first meeting half a century ago. He, then a young don at Oxford, and I a still younger don at Cambridge, spent a happy day forecasting the effects upon Christendom of the new knowledge of the origin and development of life on earth ; and for both of us the subject influenced our thinking even when in the thirties the Churches seemed to abandon it. For me Teilhard's books have renewed, and gone far towards answering, the questions. It only needed a three months' visit to Cincinnati and the renewal of contact with Teilhard's intimate friend Dr. George Barbour to turn my interest into enthusiasm. Any reader of Barbour's article on him " At work in the field " in the recently published American volume *The World of Teilhard* (Baltimore, 1961) will know the source of my thrill.

Teilhard, of course, thinks and writes in French, in the language and ideas of his friends Édouard Le Roy and Maurice Blondel, eminent members of the French Academy and exponents of a religious philosophy still expanding its influence. Through them he was in close touch with the thought and scholarship of his own country : through his travels he met and worked with the learned of many nations and races. But as all his friends insist, he was also a bold and independent thinker, original in his observations, sensitive to new ideas, and persistent in his efforts to give them accurate expression. No one who knew him has questioned his complete sincerity and honesty. His modesty and loyalty to his Church and Society made it impossible for him to protest against the sentences of banishment and silence which met his efforts to present the case for evolution and for the scientific humanists with whom he worked and whose difficulties he understood and strove to explain.

Unfortunately, as we all know, French is not a language easy to translate exactly into English ; French scientists and philosophers from Lamarck [1] onwards have suffered grievously at our hands in consequence. Teilhard has plainly been misrepresented in certain places by the too literal rendering of his technicalities. In such cases a paraphrase such as I have submitted may be the least inadequate way to interpret his thought. In citing his untranslated work I have been helped most generously by his and my friend, Dr. Tindell Hopwood, who knew him for many years, worked in the same field of palaeontology, has had much experience in translating him, and has read my book in proof.

[1] Cf., e.g., H. Graham Cannon, *Lamarck and Modern Genetics* (Manchester, 1959), pp. 10–31, on the meaning of *besoin*.

Preface

No one can begin to study Teilhard without the help of the magnificently thorough and complete record of his life and experiences, his work and writings, by his friend Dr. Claude Cuénot, son of the eminent biologist Lucien, whose death touched Teilhard deeply. The skill with which Dr. Cuénot has followed up every possible clue, his patience in extracting quotations from Teilhard's multitudinous pamphlets, letters and memoranda, his ingenuity in weaving the records of this much-travelled and crowded life into a picture of its manifold activities and his mastery of vivid detail make his work a monumental tribute. He has now (March 1962) followed it by a smaller book, admirably condensed and illustrated and with a bibliography and *vocabulaire*.[1] And what he knows, he is ready to share with an unfailing generosity. His letters to me and my notes of his conversation have been invaluable, and my contacts with him and with Mlle Mortier have been happy memories.

This encyclopaedic biography and the three volumes of letters collected and edited by Teilhard's cousin, the late Marguerite Teillard-Chambon, a trained historian, who wrote under the name of Claude Aragonnès and herself received the whole correspondence lately published as *Genèse d'une pensée* and revealing most clearly his growth and greatness during the years of his war-service, 1914–19, are indispensable to any who would understand him and unique in their disclosure of his character. They are compensation for the life-long series to his invalid sister which she decided were too intimate to publish. The two earlier books have been combined and translated as *Letters from a Traveller*.[2]

Of his friends in Cambridge, Dr. Dorothy Garrod, formerly our Professor of Archaeology, and Mr. Miles Burkitt accompanied him on his first "dig" at Castillo in 1913 and have helped me with useful information and comments. Dr. Garrod, who kept in touch with him till his death, lent me her own cyclostyled copies of four of his most significant

[1] In *Écrivains de toujours* (Seuil).   [2] Collins, 1962.

unpublished writings. Dr. T. T. Paterson, now of Glasgow University, who accompanied him in Central Asia and met him on his last visits to England, has been in touch with me. Dr. Joseph Needham, who met him in Paris when they both came back from China in 1944, has given me help about his work there and a copy of his own admirable review of the *Phenomenon* : few if any scientists are so well qualified to speak of Teilhard's philosophy and humanism.

On his palaeontology my colleagues at the British Museum, and especially Professor D. M. S. Watson of University College, London, and Dr. Tindell Hopwood, have given me details of his activities and insight into his personality, and Dr. Errol White and Dr. Kenneth Oakley have shared with me their specialised knowledge of the intriguing mystery of the Piltdown skull—a detective problem worthy of Austin Freeman.

Of friends in the Society of Jesus, Father Pierre Leroy the biologist and geneticist of the Collège de France, who has sent us his delightful book of reminiscences of Teilhard, Father R. Leys the patristic scholar of Louvain where Teilhard had many close contacts, and Father C. C. Martindale of Farm Street, the great preacher who saw him regularly in London and Paris, have given me much encouragement and evidence of his problems and position. I can only wish that I were better qualified to understand the discipline and inner life of their Society. They have opened up for me what was previously a closed field of vision. From them as from many others like Mme de Wespin who knew him in China and now edits the *Revue Teilhard* in Brussels, Dr. Gervase Mathew of Oxford and Dr. Georges Crespy whose book on Teilhard's theology only reached me when my own work was in draft, I have come to verify and establish the conviction of Teilhard's outstanding importance and his integrated understanding of our human experience.

Without my wife's insight and interest, her patience with what has at times amounted in me to an obsession, and her wide acquaintance not only with Teilhard's background but with many of his friends in France and Belgium this book could never have been undertaken and certainly never carried to publication.

For me it has meant a happy return to the subject which has always been my primary concern ; the renewal of hopes which have long been disappointed and repressed ; and the thrill of discovering new prospects and horizons and a new seer. It has been a fine sequel to work which began with the noblest of Greek heretics, Apollinarius of Laodicea, went forward to our great Anglican prophet Frederic Denison Maurice and his friend John Malcolm Ludlow, was heavily involved with John Ray the naturalist and his predecessors, and has now been concentrated upon the man who has gone furthest in resolving the basic problem which the Greeks called " the one and the many " and which to-day as " individualism and communism " divides human politics or, as what Professor C. H. Waddington [1] calls " the atomistic and the continuum theories ", besets the world of science. Teilhard, whose language is of complexification and convergence, has restated for us the position which has always inspired Christian culture since the New Testament and which denies that the paradox is ultimate or the contrast valid. For him, as for the succession to which he belongs, the many and the one are indissolubly united and mutually complementary ; the recognition of their relationship is the supreme need of to-day ; and only in the acknowledgment of world-unity, of individual integration, and of universal community can we find the way " onward and upward ". It is the clue to his solution that he sees for the whole process of evolution not only an interpretation as a cosmogenesis, but a means of attainment as a Christification.

It does not fall within the scope of this book nor the capacity of its author to discuss in any fullness the basic problems underlying this quest—those of experience and its

[1] Cf. his recent book, *The Nature of Life*, pp. 21-4.

interpretation [1]—or to contribute further to the voluminous arguments as to the meaning and character of symbolism, or the borderland between mythology and history, or the relationship between the fullness of our awareness and the abstractions of our mathematical logic. But for one who can look back to the naïve materialism of the beginning of the century, to the anti-religious humanism which succeeded it, to the logical positivism which like Socrates in his early phase probed the resulting confusion with questions, it is permissible to refer to Dr. Crespy's brilliant comment upon the resultant sterility of these cathartic remedies. [2] Speaking of Dr. Bultmann's campaign for the " demythologising " of Christianity he remarks that Dr. Bultmann demands the rejection of all religion whose interpretation conflicts with science in its most polemical and atheistic form (of which in fact he knows little) and contrasts his attitude with that of Teilhard who, testing the whole Christian claim by the standards of a science with which he is continually concerned, builds up what Bultmann would call a new mythology, but which in fact provides a horizon for science and modern man. For me, at least, it seems evident that for our interpretation of reality we must look to the fully mature, to persons who possess sensitiveness to the widest possible range of the values accessible to us ; judgment to estimate correctly both their quality and their coherence ; and intelligence aesthetic, mental and moral to demonstrate the significance of our personal experience and to find fulfilment in the love of God and of the community.

Cambridge, May 1962   *Charles E. Raven*

---

[1] I may be permitted to refer to the second volume of my Gifford Lectures published with this title in 1953.
[2] *Pensée théologique de Teilhard*, p. 168.

Contents

CHAPTER ONE

INTRODUCTORY:
TWO WORLDS, OR ONE

THE FASCINATION—and the scandal—of the life and work of Father Pierre Teilhard de Chardin arise from a single source. This is not primarily due either to his scientific support of a thoroughgoing evolutionism or to his religious insight into the experiences and significance of life, but to the fact that he, though a denizen of the two worlds which the Western peoples have treated for the past four centuries as rigidly distinct, has functioned happily in them both, has insisted that they are in fact one and the same, and has succeeded in living without a trace of schizophrenia, indeed with a remarkable integrity and completeness. He is on any showing a man of outstanding vitality and nobility of character ; of humour and modesty, valour and fortitude ; free from self-assertions or careerism ; of brilliant intellectual gifts, a thinker and according to his French contemporaries a master of their language ; of wide and original knowledge both of the whole field of natural phenomena and of the physical and psychological problems of individual and corporate life ; a mystic and something of a saint ; one who under the handicap of long exile and intense strain, and forbidden by the Society to which he was pledged and by the Church which refused discussion of his plea, to hold any office or publish during his lifetime any of his writings, yet was never embittered or rebellious. Such a man is sufficiently rare to be easily misunderstood, though the accusation of self-deception made against him by a British opponent could only have proceeded from one who had never met any of his friends, had hardly read a line of his writings in French, or else was one of those folk who do not know what honesty means. Teilhard may be mistaken in explaining his ideas : even so he is " all of a piece " and, alike in science and in religion, transparently sincere.

To-day the easy assumption, still affirmed by the more materialistic of scientists or the more dualistic of theologians, that between science and religion there is an unbridgeable chasm and therefore an essential antagonism, has become not merely out of date but intellectually hard to sustain. The collapse of behaviourism (which always involved an initial contradiction in terms) followed by the recognition that psychology, though recognising psychogenic influences upon physical conditions, was yet in the full sense a science, and leading up to the general acceptance of a psychosomatic philosophy among those best qualified to deal with persons and their nature, has left the mechanistic humanists in a precarious position. We may admit that Christians and others who claim that the conflicts of the past three centuries are now over, too often select the evidence on both sides to promote this wishful thinking ; they are at least premature and in fact often mistaken in their jubilation. But those of us who have always maintained that the Baconian contrast between science as based upon observation and experiment and religion as issuing from " the infallible oracles of God " was an unchristian fallacy can now feel that the difficulties still remaining can be faced with integrity and that a full measure of genuine co-operation can be accepted and offered. The case of Teilhard, as anyone knows who is familiar with the attitude towards him in Belgium and France, is very much in point : Catholics and Freethinkers alike realise his importance and are agreed upon his honesty : only the sceptical Englishman who sticks to his conviction that ultimately all science is a matter of weight and measurement, or as he would say mathematics, physics and chemistry, still insists that Teilhard " does not even preserve

the common decencies of scientific writing " ; sneers that in
any case his sort of science does not stand very high ; and
concludes that " I have read and studied *The Phenomenon of
Man* with real distress, even with despair. If it were an inno-
cent passive gullibility, it would be excusable : but all too
clearly, alas, it is an active willingness to be deceived." [1]

It is an interesting comment upon such an attack to read
Teilhard's own criticism of such scientists. He had, as his many
English and Scottish friends know, an almost exaggerated love
of Britain and esteem for its people : but among many tributes
to them Cuénot feels bound to include the following estimate.
" These Anglo-Saxons show themselves as notably learned,
but embedded in their scientism, positivism, empiricism, neo-
darwinianism : with few exceptions they are incapable of
following philosophical thought." [2]   One who has spent a
long life in Cambridge and received boundless kindness from
many great scientists is glad to feel that such a verdict is too
sweeping : but it is still not wholly unjust. The inevitable
specialisation and the meticulous concentration that science
to-day involves leave little room for the development of wider
and more generalised interests. Charles Darwin is not the
only one to confess : " It is an accursed evil to a man to become
so absorbed in any subject as I am in mine." [3] Sometimes his
successors neither realise the defects of their qualities nor exercise his restraint in refraining from trespassing into fields with
which they are necessarily ill-acquainted. Their devotion to
the two famous instruments, Occam's razor and Nelson's tele-
scope, is only too familiar. Both were fully employed at the
Darwin centenary meetings in London.

The plain fact, of course, is that the majority of the leaders

---

[1] This piece of emotional invective was printed in *Mind*, LXX, No. 277,
pp. 99–106. For it, see below Chapter Eleven, p. 214n. The habit of conceal-
ing ignorance by scurrility is becoming common ; and Teilhard (in translation) is a victim : cf. *Sunday Times* of 17th September 1961, " The Tertiary
Humanists ".

[2] C. Cuénot, *Teilhard de Chardin*, p. 198—quoted hereafter as Cuénot.

[3] *Life of C. D.*, II, p. 139.

of science at the present day were taught by men of my generation for whom in their own University days the two worlds
were in head-on collision. I can testify that in the first decade
of this century it was almost impossible for an honest and
intelligent s:udent to be both religious and scientific ; for the
prevailing attitude was then still that of the Renaissance which
H. G. Collingwood so admirably describes in *The Idea of
Nature*. He has pointed out that in the Classical period of
Greece and Rome—and indeed also of Israel—the natural world
or macrocosm was regarded as organic and alive, analogous
in structure and function to its microcosm, the human individual. Each consisted of an inanimate body and of an
animating mind. Injury and ignorance might destroy the
harmony between the two and dethrone the controlling reason
from its proper influence. But the earth, like its inhabitants,
was normally responsible and orderly. In consequence there
was real science of a high order ; and technology, if not yet
elaborate, had at least learnt the exactitudes of the design of
the Parthenon and the construction of the Roman aqueducts.
Those who sneer at Aristotle or Archimedes or the Hippo-
cratic Colleges reveal only their own ignorance.

What the Renaissance accomplished was not the discovery
of the so-called scientific method—that is as old as cookery
and fundamental to all human thinking. It was the conviction
that if nature itself were treated not as an organism but as a
machine, certain improvements in the setting and resources of
life could be easily developed. Observation and experiment
are as old as mankind ; the application of them to simple
mechanical inventions was fascinating and useful. Science,
which to the Greeks had included all exercise of the intellect,
now began to be confined to the realm of weight and measurement. By the end of the seventeenth century steam-power
gave us a new range of instruments ; fifty years later the
machine had supplied the symbol not only of human effort
but of human nature. When the cynical J. de la Mettrie, author

of *L'Homme-machine* (1748),[1] accused Albrecht Haller the
pioneer of physiology of being responsible for his materialism,
the charge seemed monstrous to those who knew Haller's
devotedly religious sincerity. But in fact the whole approach
to biological problems was then, and indeed has been until
very recently, strictly and dogmatically mechanistic.

Nevertheless, in Western Europe generally since Bergson,
and in Britain since the 1920s, the attempt to confine science
to purely material categories has broken down. The New
Physics with its abandonment of the closed universe, and
the New Psychology with its insistence upon the importance of psychogenic causation and personal relationships,
paved the way for the full recognition of the coexistence
of the two worlds, material and immaterial. The greatest
of British medical physiologists, Sir Charles Sherrington,
in his Gifford Lectures *Man on his Nature*, set out the traditionally scientific description of humanity, and to each
count of it attached another description in terms of personality
and appreciation ; made it evident that neither could be rejected ; and if he hardly succeeded in reconciling them, convinced any intelligent reader that both were valid and essential
to a full understanding of mankind. Conwy Lloyd Morgan,
Vice-Chancellor of Bristol University and the pioneer of comparative psychology, following a clue from G. H. Lewis,
brought the two worlds into vital union and expounded in his
Emergent Evolution the continuity of the creative process, the
concomitance of body and spirit, and the reality of progress
and novelty. As we shall see, his schema was almost exactly
identical on its scientific side with that of Teilhard. Field-
Marshal Smuts, scholar, soldier and statesman, had written his
Holism and Evolution and set out the philosophy of which his
life and policies were the expression, a philosophy very similar
to Teilhard's exposition of complexity and convergence.
Collingwood in his chapters on the modern idea of nature

[1] He was among the first to assert the transition from animals to man
and the kinship of men and apes (cf. J. Rostand, *L'Homme*, pp. 23-5).

gives a full account of this new attitude and discusses its most important exponents. On the religious side Lionel Thornton, John Oman and perhaps William Temple are representatives of the new organic and personalistic outlook ; of the doctors Sir Russell Brain is at once the most satisfying and the most influential, and to him more than to most we owe the concept of a psychosomatic universe.

It is obvious that this idea of nature involves for us all a recognition of the wholeness of experience, the continuity of evolution, the relation of the many to the one, and the power of man increasingly to guide and accelerate the creative process ; a recognition which Teilhard has consistently and fully represented. For many of us this acceptance of the unity and coherence of the cosmos has been a commonplace, ever since the ablest of British philosophers, Samuel Alexander and Alfred North Whitehead, expounded it. But it is obvious that to very many of the scientists and the theologians who take leading parts in the controversies that still devastate the meeting-points of their respective territories, a strict apartheid is the only rule —and the consequent arguments generate more heat than light. The theologians still discourse as if the music of the spheres or even of the fiddles had no necessary relationship with the instruments that transmit it, while the scientists in their professional capacity still insist in spite of James Hinton that the only explanation of a violin concerto must be in terms of " the scraping of the tails of horses on the intestines of cats." [1] The two worlds could hardly be more rigidly isolated.

It is this dualism, more than the scientific method, which was popularised by the mechanical ingenuities of Grosseteste and Roger Bacon and brought to triumph by Galileo and Descartes. Science in its true sense is as old as mankind, indeed a rudimentary accompaniment of conscious life. To learn by trial and error, that is by observation and experiment, is not

[1] *Life of J. H.*, p. 139 ; cf. Havelock Ellis, *Impressions and Comments*, II, pp. 139–41.

the perquisite of the mammal but, as Lloyd Morgan proved, of newly-hatched chicks ; indeed as we now must admit of insects and perhaps even down to protozoa. It is present wherever there is any degree of discrimination or of choice between one form of food and another. To say that the Greeks had no science because they were not deeply concerned with technology is of course to ignore their immense contributions to medicine and anatomy, to architecture and sculpture, ceramics and music, geometry and mathematics, zoology and botany, psychology and philosophy. Only those who still try to confine science to weight and measurement can write about religion and science as having nothing in common.

The scientists who take this view still seem to be fairly numerous in America, where behaviourism is a not infrequent type of psychology and where thinking in terms of black and white is notably and passionately common. In Europe, whatever be the case in Russia, gadget-mongering and mechanistic analogies are much less dominant. In Britain, the struggle in physics was settled quietly in an atmosphere already sweetened by men like Clerk Maxwell, Lord Kelvin and Sir Joseph Thomson, when Einstein's theories of relativity destroyed the doctrine of the closed universe. But in biology, where Darwin's theory of survival by automatic sifting was reinforced on its deterministic side by the early geneticists, it cost some twenty years of struggle before the new psychologists convinced medical and physiological schools of their right to be treated as scientists. In zoology, probably until lately the most materialistic of the sciences, there is still too much of the old dogmatism and evasiveness, the *odium theologicum* of the ecclesiastic and the invectives of the heresy-hunter.

But to admit that there is still controversy, and that this will remain until both sides have not only abandoned their exclusiveness but reformed their claims, is not to suggest that the whole relationship has not changed quite enormously in recent years. In England indeed there has never been the sharp antagonism and civil strifes of other European countries : and this not simply because of our indifference or muddle-headedness or genius for compromise, but thanks to the lack of credal tests in most of our Free Churches and to the long succession of scholars in the Anglican Communion who have stood for comprehension and a reasonable faith ever since the days of the Cambridge Platonists. It may be doubted whether any denomination in Christendom has in the past century done more to explore and interpret the two chief movements of our time, the social revolution and the scientific and technological transformation. From Maurice and Ludlow through Westcott and Scott Holland and Gore, to Mansbridge and Tawney and Temple, or from Kingsley and Hort through Lloyd Morgan and Barnes, and Tennant, to the recent author of *A Scientist who believes in God* [1] there has never till the last twenty-five years been a lack of Churchmen qualified to speak with authority in these fields.

Nor must we be influenced by the present failure among us to maintain our demonstration of the unity of the two worlds. The strain and losses of the First World War, reinforced by the inability to fulfil its pledges or to establish a generous peace or to avert political and economic disasters, broke the nerves of those who had survived the carnage and distorted the qualities of the young. Theology, history and philosophy were infected by the prevailing pessimism. There was small help from literature or the arts. Even the world of science though making great advances in technology did little to relieve and much to endanger the maladies of men and nations. Only medicine, the one profession which deals inescapably with persons, kept its courage and power to heal. The period named by the late Professor E. L. Allen as that of " the great blight " [2] from 1936 onwards was at once the proof and the penalty of our loss of nerve. But even so the Second

---

[1] By H. N. V. Temperley, published by Hodder and Stoughton, 1961.

[2] Cf. his essay " British Theology and the Great Blight " in *Religion in Britain since 1900* (London, 1952), pp. 182–97, which examines the character and effects of what is usually called Biblical Theology or Barthianism.

World War disclosed that the disease was not mortal ; despite Belsen and Auschwitz, Hiroshima and Nagasaki, the common people of the resistance movements or of the blitzed cities showed a valour and endurance prophetic of a new social order. A religion of despair, the rhetoric of Dr. Reinhold Niebuhr or the exegesis of Dr. Barth, did not fairly represent and could not adequately inspire the fortitude and hopes of such a world. Even now when the effects of their despair still combine to prevent us from realising the grandeur of our opportunities and the compelling signs of hope, we are recovering the faith which underlay the failures of the twenties and suggests the adventures which the revolutionary changes of our world encourage.

Such an interlude in the thought and life of the Church, disappointing as it has been to those who realise not only that the progress of evangelism has been frustrated but that the primary work of Christendom has been distorted, must be seen against the background of the Second World War with its unprecedented savagery, its destruction of civilian and hitherto generally respected security, its disruption of all normal peace-time activities and its laying of new and absorbing duties upon the clergy and churches. Those whose work was concerned with a pastoral or theological ministry found themselves caught up into the problems of evacuation and fire-watching, of supplying help to schools, hospitals, the homeless, the blitzed, and the members of the forces, of serving and suffering with a world at war. No wonder if, like Archbishop Temple, they had to abandon the large objectives and the wide vision in favour of restricted and anachronistic doctrines, if to meet the cruelties and barbarisms of total war they had to return in theology to the " Lord God " of *Green Pastures* and to invent in apologetic the new dogma of " strategic necessity ". Surely if men could plan and perpetrate such diabolisms, the earth could not be the Lord's but only a successfully rebellious province of his domain, temporarily ceded to Satan and his hosts. So we had to accept the total transcendence of God, to transform the Incarnation into belief in a " divine intruder ", to revive mediaeval ideas of the Fall and Atonement, to denounce Natural Religion as pagan and confine the activity of the Holy Spirit to the visible and institutional Church. An unpleasant consequence of this change was the misrepresentation and contempt poured not only upon all who could be labelled as modernists or liberals but upon the great scholars and prophets of the first two decades of the century. Libelling the dead has become common among novelists : it is not rare among Christians.

It is necessary to speak plainly of this blight. During the twenties in Britain, though the Universities were at a low ebb and the Churches had been bled white of their ablest recruits, there was a real and widespread effort to redeem the time. From the Archbishops' Recruiting Campaign in 1919 to the Way of Renewal in 1931 there was a succession of movements testifying to the vision and vitality of the Churches. The COPEC movement of 1920–24, the Conferences at Stockholm, Lausanne and Jerusalem, and the plans for the United Church of South India proved the international character of the Christian programme. At the same time theology in the wider sense of the word was attempting the unexplored fields of social and evolutionary interpretation ; and the traditional acceptance of class-privileges and industrial exploitations, of conventional orthodoxies and contempt for science was being seriously challenged. In the more intimate field attention was centred upon the historical study of the New Testament and the person of Christ, but this was set against a coherent doctrine of Creation and accompanied by a series of books aiming at a deeper understanding of the Holy Spirit and the unity of the whole creative, redemptive, sanctifying process in a sacramental and holistic universe. This involved a new and friendly study of other religions and a presentation of Christianity as uniquely representative rather than aggressively exclusive in its claims.

The International Missionary Council at Jerusalem and the

World Call to the Churches which followed it in 1928 marked the zenith of this movement. Its collapse came in fact suddenly. The economic disaster in 1930 which brought almost total unemployment to the coalfields and shipyards and cotton mills and so to heavy industry in general, reduced large parts of Britain to destitution and destroyed such hope as still remained of those better days for which the war had professedly been waged. The sabotage by the United States of President Wilson's policies and of the League of Nations was completed by the financial panic and world-wide devastation of the Republican supremacy. When it became evident that German democracy was being overthrown and Italy had become Fascist, a despair like that which the Gothic invasions and the fall of Rome in A.D. 410 had brought to the Church in the days of Jerome and Augustine settled upon Western Christendom. The "new orthodoxy" concentrated upon sin, declared the world to be totally corrupt and God's Kingdom an eschatological dream, denied reality to the idea of progress and value to human reason and effort, and reduced theology to a Calvinistic insistence upon God's inscrutable and predestinating omnipotence. The evangelising of the nations was superseded by the redemption of the elect ; the doctrines of Natural Religion, of the creative process and of the indwelling Spirit were denounced : a great preacher held forth about Moral Man and Immoral Society ; a Gifford lecturer castigated the possibility of natural theology ; and the popular literature of the Churches was supplied by laity without any particular training in science, history or philosophy. It is an interesting symptom of the effects of this collapse that Christ's religion became almost wholly confined to Scripture treated as the single means of revelation and to liturgy as the single activity of the Church. In the former case history and philosophy in the wider sense were almost ignored ; in the latter, social service and "good works" were left to the secular agencies. In universities and the professions a type of humanism, explicitly anti-supernatural if not anti-religious, became dominant and the former concern with the historic Jesus and the Gospel of the Kingdom of God was neglected if not denounced.

An example of this can be found even in the story of the development of Anglican theology between 1889 and 1939 entitled *From Gore to Temple*, by Archbishop A. M. Ramsey. Here we have a searching exposition of theological writers and books that deal with the central doctrines of Incarnation and Atonement. The selection is of course personal, and on occasion the memories become enthusiastic although the commentary remains objective and often illuminating. But the significant point is that the subjects which seem to many of us absolutely vital—the commending of the faith in relation to the new social order and to the new cosmology—are rarely even mentioned. The theology of God as Creator and of God as the Holy Spirit hardly receive any notice, except in the case of L. S. Thornton's *The Incarnate Lord* which is recognised as showing contact with contemporary thought but which the Archbishop never discusses and of which he does not seem to realise the inconsistencies. His choice of writers and his mode of exposition disclose that he seems to have little appreciation of the fact that doctrine can never become the abstract presentation of a system, but must be an instrument for continuing the reconciling of men to God in Christ. Neither Gore nor Temple would have been content to see their theology so stripped of its social and intellectual reference. The Archbishop treats Christian truth as if it were still measurable by the disputations of the patristic age or of the Reformation, although in summarising the position since the close of his survey he seems to admit that the period since 1939 has been a sad one—"The isolation of Biblical theology is very plain . . . its contact with the age is sometimes far to seek."[1] Moreover, and very significantly, he quotes with approval Temple's words, "One day theology will take up again its larger and serener task, and offer to a new Christendom its Christocentric metaphysic."[2] Per-

---

[1] *From Gore to Temple*, pp. 168–9.   [2] L.c. p. 161.

28

haps we may claim that Teilhard has now initiated this very thing. The response to him has plainly renewed the hopes which have been delayed, if not abandoned, in the last twenty-five years. If so, though the " blight" will remain, its effects may not be wholly a loss.

For though it helped to destroy the evangelistic fervour of the Student Volunteer Missionary Union, the reforming passion of the Christian Socialists, and the evolutionary theology of the 1920s, it has reminded us of the cost and conditions of our redemption, of the extent of our individual arrogance and corporate corruption, and of the futility of a glib and shallow optimism. It is a strange fact that the First World War which to Teilhard and to most of those actually under fire disclosed not only the tragedy and evil of our humanity, but also and compellingly its fortitude and fellowship, should have meant for others, and especially for those with no immediate experience of battle, only the depravity and helplessness of mankind as a whole, and the sin and folly of its individual components. That Teilhard and Barth should have been contemporaries, each deeply affected by his wartime environment is enough to warn us of the dilemma which lies in the depths of human thought and life. Their responses to it represent the problem of the two worlds in its clearest Christian form. We must recognise the sincerity and the convictions of the Barthian message of God's " otherness" and man's impotence, even if we must deplore its theology and much of its effects. What we find hardest to accept is that the Protestant world enthroned Barth while the Vatican exiled and did its best to silence Teilhard. Of the contrast between them Teilhard was of course well aware, though he seldom mentions Barth.[1]

---

[1] *Letters from a Traveller* (London, 1962), p. 354.

CHAPTER TWO

TEILHARD AND HIS FRENCH
BACKGROUND

AN ENGLISHMAN even if a younger contemporary of Pierre
Teilhard de Chardin will not find it easy to discover the formative influences under which his remarkable combination of
religious, scientific and literary interests was fostered and
developed into so richly integrated a personality. The facts
of his early life are well known.[1] Born on the 1st May 1881
at his family home at Sarcenat some three miles west of
Clermont-Ferrand in the Auvergne ; the fourth of the eleven
children of Emmanuel Teilhard de Chardin and on his mother's
side the sixth direct descendant of Voltaire's sister ; his father
a gentleman-farmer, of ancient race, skilled in agriculture,
learned in local lore and antiquities, interested in books and
natural history, a collector of birds, insects and geological
specimens, quiet, kindly and widely respected ; his mother,
lovable, cultured and deeply religious. He inherited from
them both a tradition of happy family-life and a delight in
the hill-country and volcanic cones of the district, in the
simplicity and independence of its life, the rigours of its winters,
and the hard exercise which fitted him for the explorations
and adventures of his later years. There is the bare setting :
the booklet on his beloved sister Marguerite-Marie called *The*

---

[1] The monumental biography by Dr. Claude Cuénot (Plon, Paris,
1958) is indispensable. Abbé Paul Grenet has published a small volume with
a condensed account of his travels but a disappointing study of his thought
(Seghers, Paris, 1961).

30

Energy of Suffering speaks of its influence.[1] For education he went in 1892 to the Jesuit college of Mongré at Villefranche ; in 1899 he entered the Order and after a period of ill-health went to Aix for his novitiate ; in 1902 when anti-clericalism was at its zenith he moved to their school in Jersey ; but it is difficult to gather what was his own outlook or how his very wide range of insight and interests was encouraged. Dr. Cuénot's excellent biography though it mentions the stages of his education and the names of those who were directly associated with him does not describe the atmosphere or the intellectual climate of his adolescence. He had brains and charm, a quick tongue and a sense of humour, got on well with his work and with his companions, passed his tests with distinction but had plenty of power in reserve, and was always devoted to the rocks and to God. But his friend and comrade of later years, the Jesuit scientist Pierre Leroy, in his delightful memoir adds that only in the religious instruction at school did he fail ; and that this was due to the traditional and senti-mental character of the teaching.[2]

When he went to Jersey he was already showing interest in the principles of science, the " symbolisme " of Pierre Duhem and the " commodisme " of Henri Poincaré ; his religious life was guided by the *Imitatio* : and he belonged to a small group of outstanding boys in which his chief friends were Pierre Charles, afterwards at Louvain [3] and Auguste Valensin [4] with whom he was in contact until shortly before his own death. Indeed, in July 1946 he amazed Valensin by telling him, " It is to you that I owe my ideas—to what you said to me in Jersey." [5]

[1] By Monique Givelet, 1951. Cf. for this C. Cuénot, l.c. p. 12.
[2] *Teilhard de C., tel que ie l'ai connu*, pp. 12–13.
[3] For their future contact cf. Cuénot, p. 150.
[4] Cf. Cuénot, p. 19, and *Letters from a Traveller*, p. 348 note, and Teil-hard's letter ; and above all the recently published *Auguste Valensin ; textes et documents*, pp. 133, 200, etc. In this book, p. 336, it is reported that Teilhard's letters to Valensin have been preserved and may be published.
[5] L.c. p. 335.

After his three years devoted to philosophy in Jersey he was appointed for his *régence* as lecturer in chemistry and physics to the Jesuit College in Cairo where he also had charge of the museum. His colleague Joseph Clainpanain was also a keen naturalist, and the two made many expeditions, Teilhard for fossils of which he made some interesting discoveries, and his companion for molluscs and insects. The three years there gave him his first experience of a hot climate and of desert conditions but were otherwise uneventful : A. Alfieri, afterwards Secretary of the Entomological Society of Egypt, was their pupil, and Cuénot [1] prints a letter from him recalling their work.

His final phase of training, the four years dedicated to theology, were spent at the Jesuit centre, Ore Place near Hastings : and there his development in all respects became rapid and important. It was then that the main lines of his scientific and of his religious work and character were settled. But of this later.

Before we consider his friends and their significance or his relationship to the thinkers among them, one of his chief characteristics must be noted—his independence of outlook and care in protecting himself in life and thought from undue external pressures or influences. He was alert and observant, but, still more, scrupulous about estimating the significance of what he had seen and slow to accept explanations of it at second-hand. His thought is not only never a thing of shreds and patches, but whatever its relative importance always primarily his own. He was immensely ready to give and receive ideas, to discuss and enquire and explain : but he would make his way to their significance by his own road. Father Leroy who was with him at a very critical stage in his life makes this characteristic very plain : " I believe one can say ", he writes,[2] " that his synthesis has always been conceived progressively and without any *maître à penser*." Once recognised, this explains both his consistency of de-

development and his occasional slowness in reaching a new conclusion.

One point about his youth which will at once strike an Englishman is that in spite of his love of nature and his study of fossil-life he was apparently unaware of the controversies over Darwin, or indeed of the whole subject of evolution until he was close on thirty. By that time he had collected and even written about prehistoric plants and animals in Jersey and while teaching in Egypt, and must surely have been at least concerned with the descent of man both in its scientific and its religious significance. Yet he remained a believer in the traditional idea of creation until his time at the Jesuit training college at Ore. How could this have happened ?

The fact is that between French and English philosophy at that time and until Bergson there was not any close contact ; and from the Catholic standpoint our point of view was not of a kind which a candidate for the priesthood would study. The cleavage between the Christian tradition and the new knowledge which characterised the whole civilisation of the nineteenth century, took the form in France of a fierce intellectual and theological struggle between Catholic dogma and the critical study of Scripture and the Creeds. In this area it reached its crisis for Churchmen in the condemnation of Alfred Loisy's books in 1903. In England the battleground was over Darwin between science and religion and this had not then spread far across the Channel among Catholics. For the educated Frenchman Herbert Spencer was almost the only British philosopher to be widely known, and he was identified with evolution [1]—that is with his own particular interpretation of that word. Not unnaturally, his theories were exposed to attack and in any case he was not in favour among Christians. Yet even to-day he still has an importance in French thought

---

[1] In France *transformisme* has been the term applied to the problems to which we have tended to restrict " evolution ". Lamarck and Darwin are to the French " transformistes " ; Spencer is the founder of " evolutionist'' philosophy.

such as in England hardly outlived his death. It is not surprising that coming across the Channel under these auspices the strength and importance of Darwin's theory should have been largely unfamiliar. It is significant that no allusion to the subject had ever been made by the Vatican until the publication of Pius XII's Encyclical *Humani generis* in 1950 [1] and that evolution, which to almost all the English-speaking world is now a fact, is elsewhere still only a scientific hypothesis. For Teilhard it was not until his years in Sussex that he had strong experience of the unity and continuity of the world of nature and that he found in Bergson's *Creative Evolution* a convincing interpretation of it.[2]

This, though it led him to a full acceptance of creation as an evolutionary process in which we were wholly involved, did not for many years influence his method of interpreting it. He worked out his vocabulary in France as we shall see and in terms of which the most important were " *complexification* " and " *convergence* ". By the former he denoted the tendency at all levels for the units to develop increasingly complex structures, atoms in the molecule, molecules in the cell, cells in the organism—a complexity accompanied by an increase of conscious awareness. The latter was already used in mathematics, and in biology in France though not in England, except by one lonely zoologist Arthur Willey [3] whose book *Convergent Evolution* published in 1902 gave it a wide application to trends in " habits, functions, structure and physiognomy ". Teilhard and his friends employed it regularly to describe the tendency of individual organisms under a similar and definite environmental challenge to produce convergent and ultimately identical results. This is a meaning hardly known to British

---

[1] This occasioned Teilhard's paper *Monogénisme et monophylétisme*.

[2] Teilhard recognised and discussed this in a pamphlet on *Cosmogenèse*, cf. Cuénot, pp. 352–4. For further discussion of this subject see below, Chapter Seven.

[3] A Cambridge scholar who did much original work in Ceylon and then became Professor of Zoology at McGill University.

biologists until very lately.[1] Teilhard's friend, H. F. Osborn, though he used it, put a very restricted meaning upon it ; and this is also found in some French scientists. As will be evident, the linguistic difficulty is not easy to resolve for Teilhard's readers : for himself it meant a departure from Bergson, a concentration upon convergence at the level of human development, upon the concept of the noosphere or realm of self-conscious " unanimisation ", and so upon the ideas of the " Omega Point ", of " amorisation " and " Christification ".

In France moreover, as we have noted, the cleavage between Catholic and Secularist, always deeper and more divisive than analogous divisions in England, had produced under Émile Combes strongly anti-religious feelings and policies. But there was a movement among the educated which promised a new and more creative outlook and a healthier and more vigorous life. If we ask how it was that in the period between 1912 and 1923 the young Teilhard not only found the splendid courage of his war service but also laid firm foundations for his remarkable interpretation of an evolutionary, integrated and strongly Christian philosophy, the answer can best be studied in the light of his closest and most intimate teacher and partner the eminent scholar and thinker Édouard Le Roy (1870–1954).

The clearest evidence of this is perhaps to be found in the first volume of Le Roy's last book *Essai d'une philosophie première*, in the chapters dealing with Nature (3rd part, pp. 330–433). Here he three times [2] quoted Teilhard's first published essay on evolution, *Comment se pose aujourd'hui la question de transformisme?*,[3] which must have been one of their earliest subjects of discussion, then quoted his paper of January 1925, *Le Paradoxe transformiste*,[4] a criticism of L. Vialleton's

[1] Cf. C. F. A. Pantin, "Terrestrial Nemertines and Evolutionary Convergence", etc.

[2] Pp. 339, 344 and 354.

[3] In *Études*, t. 167, pp. 524–44, June 1921.

[4] In *Revue des Questions Scientifiques*, 7, pp. 53–80, quoted on p. 358.

attack upon evolution, and finally, after a passage in which he deals with the culmination of the whole process in the phenomenon of man, added a note on p. 413, " In what precedes I have hardly done more than repeat almost textually an unpublished work of Father Teilhard in which he has expressed the results of our shared meditations ". But apparently it was under the influence of Abbé Gaudefroy, Professor at the Institut, that Teilhard met Le Roy, and this did not lead to any important results immediately : their close friendship only began after his first visit to China. But from 1925 when he developed his concept of the noosphere till Le Roy's death in 1954 they were intimately associated, and Cuénot gives many extracts from their letters to demonstrate how completely they shared all their thoughts and discussed every problem in the whole field of philosophy and religion ; he even uses the word *symbiose* [1] to describe their relationship. In his great book, *L'Exigence idéaliste et le fait de l'évolution*, Le Roy constantly acknowledges his indebtedness [2] and Teilhard declares that his whole concept of hominisation and the noosphere was due to their joint efforts. To anyone who reads their books side by side their relationship to one another is obvious both in the structure and character of their thought and in the arguments and often the phrases in which they present it. On a detailed comparison we may perhaps feel that Teilhard has a stronger and more independent mind, and in scientific matters a clearer and more accurate knowledge with a wider range, but that Le Roy also has a profound and searching intellect and a larger understanding of relevant thinkers and books. He was also the older man and had grown up in what he describes as the France of Taine and Renan [3] with its enthusiastic but

[1] Cuénot, p. 81. It should be noted that Grenet, *Teilhard*, pp. 73-6, seems to underestimate their similarity.

[2] L.c. p. 82.

[3] Cf. " Renan investigates the origins of Christianity ; Taine writes up the origins of contemporary France ", E. Bréhier, *Transformation ou la philosophie française*, p. 11.

intolerant cult of positivist science. From this intolerance Teilhard helped him to free himself and, according to Nicolas Corte,[1] the two used to meet at Le Roy's house every Wednesday to discuss the great scientific and biological issues of the time. Daniel-Rops assigns these meetings to the years when Le Roy was preparing his books *L'Exigence idéaliste et le fait de l'évolution* (1927) and *Les Origines humaines et l'évolution de l'intelligence* (1928), though they had no doubt covered the ground of Teilhard's papers *La Vie cosmique* (1916) and *La Paléontologie et l'apparition de l'homme* (1923). It speaks volumes for the depth of their partnership that in spite of the warnings of Teilhard's friends it was not broken when in 1931 Le Roy was put on the Index.[2]

Le Roy's first and perhaps most important influence upon Teilhard was in relation to Henri Bergson. As we have seen, Teilhard had been a *fixiste* until his period of theological training at Ore Place, where he spent the four years 1909–12. During that time he step by step became convinced of the cosmic significance of evolution and was possessed by it and read *L'Évolution créatrice*.[3] The effect upon him as upon many of us at our first contact with it was revolutionary. Le Roy's evidence helps us to expand this record and is so important for an understanding of Teilhard as to be worth recapitulation.

In 1901, five years after the publication of *Mind and Memory* and six before that of *Creative Evolution*, Le Roy had written of Bergson's work that " it has been prepared by the contemporary idea of evolution which it investigates and perfects, sifting it from its ore of materialism and turning it into genuine metaphysics. Is not this the philosophy suited to the

[1] *La Vie et l'âme de Teilhard*, p. 51.

[2] By Decree dated 24th June 1931 and naming his four chief books : Bergson had been similarly condemned in 1914. Le Roy accepted the sentence without protest.

[3] Cf. *Le Cœur de la matière*, his autobiography ; and Claude Tresmontant, *Introduction à la pensée de Teilhard de C.* (Paris, 1956), pp. 26 ff., 63 ff., one of the first accounts of Teilhard's religious philosophy.

century of history ? Perhaps it indicates that a period has arrived in which mathematics losing its rôle as the regulating science is about to give place to biology." This is a very intelligent prediction of what he said at full length in 1912 when the book from which it is quoted was published in England.[1] The first half of it surveys Bergson's method and teaching, acclaiming him as the founder of a new type of philosophy and describing in some fullness the essentials of his system and in particular of his whole epistemology with its stress upon the primacy of instinct and experience, upon its development and materialisation by intellect, and upon its full expression in intuition. The two papers translated from articles in the *Revue des Deux Mondes* in February 1912 are in effect expositions of the concept of duration as set out psychologically in *Matter and Memory* and historically in *Creative Evolution*. To them in the English book are attached a series of chapters dealing with the many points on which this new philosophy opens up fresh interpretations and is liable to misunderstanding. It is a profound and sensitive study and reveals clearly how much and within what limits Teilhard was influenced by him and by Bergson. For them all, real existence was not to be attained by the intellectual formulation of fixed states arranged in a formal sequence but by immersion in " the bosom of becoming ", by experiencing existence from within the evolutionary process. So, too, conceptual analysis upon which mathematical and so-called scientific interpretation has hitherto been based, is radically different from philosophical intuition. In this inner world of pure quality there is " no measurable homogeneity, no collection of atomically constructed elements ". Only when its phases reach the surface, so to speak, and come into contact with the external world and find expression in language do material categories become applicable to them. This is, of course, Teilhard's doctrine of withinness, and a prelude to our widespread conviction to-day that true relationship is an experience of the whole personality

[1] *A New Philosophy, Henri Bergson*, p. 201.

which for purposes of interpretation and communication has to be translated into the worlds of our sense-perceptions, and represented in metaphors appropriate to them.

Where Teilhard differed from Bergson is in his refusal to draw the sharp contrast of *Creative Evolution* between the worlds of instinct and of intellect, the internal and the external. Bergson drawing much of his biological knowledge from the work of Jean Henri Fabre, " the Homer of the Insects ", " that inimitable observer " as Charles Darwin called him, accepted Fabre's evidence of the immediacy and accuracy of instinctive behaviour as, for example, in the parasitisms of the solitary wasps, and his comparison between this direct impact of life on life and our clumsy mechanisms and artifices. He regarded the developments of life as branching out into separate and often exclusive types which though they enriched also in some respects distorted the original wholeness of existence. For him, as Le Roy puts it, " Life is mental travel, ascent in a path of growing specialisation." [1] To Teilhard this meant that Bergson accepted " complexification " but left no room for " convergence ", that for him life was evolving towards increasing diversities, not into a richer and more integrated unity. Where Bergson recognised an initial instinct and a progressively estranged intellect, Teilhard saw a primal energy developing into fuller and more expressive perceptions and a more coherent and effective activity.

Moreover, because Teilhard was free from Bergson's idea of an *élan vital* constantly striving to permeate and control the obdurate and unco-operative matter of the universe, he was unable to accept in its crude form the teleology of a plan imposed from without by the life-force. Very significant in this respect is his treatment of the Scottish doctor, the friend of Smuts, H. Broom,[2] whose claim that the development of the Australopithecids follows a pre-ordained plan led to a strong criticism of natural selection and the neo-Darwinians.

[1] *A New Philosophy*, p. 122.
[2] Author of *Finding the Missing Link*, 1950.

This Teilhard rejects ; " for whether one is Lamarckian or Bergsonian one must frankly admit that even at the human level life only advances hesitatingly under the influence of great numbers and the play of chance ; [1] and if one be spiritually minded one must still recognise that the work of creation presents itself to our experience as a *process* whose laws it is the business of science to investigate, leaving to philosophy the task of discerning in the phenomenon the place and influence of an *intention*." [2] To him as to any good Darwinian the pressure of competition and the element of randomness were of obvious importance : the scientist must not ignore or replace them. But Teilhard's conviction of the dynamic unity of the cosmos and of the twin principles of convergence (the tendency towards assimilation and inter-dependence) [3] and of emergence (or the achievement of novelty) eliminated the " gladiatorial " aspect of the creative process and suggested that all the particularities combined in it contributed to the fulfilment of the cosmogenesis.

The other outstanding French thinker with whom he was in close contact after the war was Maurice Blondel, 1861–1949, whom he met first through his fellow-Jesuit Auguste Valensin. Blondel was a friend of Le Roy and a collaborator with him in the *Annales de philosophie chrétienne* and is regarded by many of our contemporaries as among the most important and creative philosophers of his time. His very distinguished academic career culminated in 1895 in the publication of the first version of his great work *L'Action*. Its range of vision and scope of contents, its penetrating insight and analysis, its originality of approach to subjects of universal importance, and its skill in developing fresh arguments to expound psychological, moral, intellectual and religious problems gave it

---

[1] This striking phrase occurs also in his *Le Cœur de la matière*. It seems to be a late element in his thought.

[2] *L'Apparition de l'homme*, pp. 179–82.

[3] Convergence has recently been used by British zoologists in a similar but slightly more specialised meaning, cf. C. F. A. Pantin and above p. 18.

immediate recognition, and fixed its author's work. For some twenty years he studied and discussed and taught, until in 1934 *La Pensée*, a treatise covering an even larger and more profound field was published and ushered in a revision of his first work and a succession of other more specialised volumes. He appreciated all the contemporary trends—existentialism and the concrete, anxiety, choice and engagement, and transcendence—and was a man of deeply Christian quality, concerned to present the Church's doctrine in language and setting appropriate to modern knowledge and needs. These qualities are admirably shown in his correspondence with Loisy and von Hügel, collected in *Au cœur de la crise moderniste*.[1]

Blondel's experience before he met Teilhard had been complementary to that of Le Roy. While Le Roy had been concerned with the impact of science upon religion and so with Bergson and the traditional cosmology, Blondel had been involved in the Modernist controversy, a similar conflict between ancient and modern arising from the impact of biblical criticism upon ecclesiastical doctrine. Here the issue had been raised by Alfred Loisy's book, *L'Évangile et l'Église*, a demand based on exegetical study for the drastic re-interpretation of the Traditional Faith. Blondel, as his *Histoire et dogme* (1904) and the recently published correspondence have proved, was probably the ablest and most impressive defender of the basic Christian theology in its attitude to the past, and was outspoken in his warnings to the rebels against it. His generous understanding of the critics and his friendship with von Hügel did not prevent him from condemning the extent and character of their revolt. Writing not so much as a historian and exegete but from his position as a Christian philosopher he developed a subtle and brilliant statement of theological orthodoxy, sensitive in its temper, profound in its insight, and fresh in its

[1] Valensin had been in close touch with Blondel since 1899 ; cf. *Correspondance entre M. Blondel et A. Valensin 1899–1912*, 2 vols. (Paris, 1957). His note introducing Teilhard to Blondel, dated 18th September 1919, is in *Auguste Valensin ; textes et documents* (Paris, 1961), p. 133.

presentation. Throughout the vast volume of his labours he showed himself able to appreciate Teilhard's problems and to provide a background for his adventures and a sense of security for his speculations—though according to Cuénot he had none of Teilhard's cosmic sense nor of his belief that the universe was in a state of cosmogenesis.[1]

For Teilhard this background was eminently congenial. In the Modernist crisis Blondel had displayed more consistently than any of his correspondents or critics an appreciation of the fullness and universality of Christ as the true image of God, the true revelation of the cosmos. He had demonstrated the extent to which historical critics like Loisy or even dedicated scholars like von Hügel were concerned with secondary though intensely important elements in the totality of the Faith, and that concentration upon these might easily distort and so impair the Pan-Christism of which he was to a unique degree the author and interpreter. The combination in him of a sense of wholeness which transcended sectional orthodoxies and modernisms with a lucid insight, a gift of exposition and a sympathetic and reconciling modesty gave him an outstanding place among those concerned with the contemporary struggle between old and new. His reference of all problems to the fact of the indwelling and cosmic Christ must have contributed very largely to Teilhard's rapid development of a Pauline and consummating *christique*. It is also probable that Blondel's experience prevented him from association with the Modernism with which in many respects he would seem to have much in common. It must not be forgotten that for Teilhard the Modernist crisis took place while he was at school ; and that later though he desired to see dogma sifted and modernised he did not want it " to evaporate into symbolism ".[2]

With Blondel, Teilhard's partnership was less intimate and

---

[1] Cf. Teilhard's letter of 15th February 1955 (Cuénot, p. 56) in which he admits the influence of Pan-Christism but claims to have arrived at this belief independently.

[2] Cuénot, p. 266.

personal than with Le Roy : it was an affair of the mind rather than of the heart. But it came at a very important stage in his development. He had finished his preparatory training and found the main lines of his message before 1914, completing it at Canterbury in the autumn of that year. Then he was flung out of his academic surroundings into the holocaust of trench-warfare. Few men of any sensitiveness can endure and none can without experience imagine the years which Teilhard spent as a stretcher-bearer on the Western Front and around Verdun ; and nowhere else can life and thought, the basic stuff of human nature, ever have been more drastically and continuously tested.[1] No one can come through such an experience without discovering in himself and the world depths and heights which compel a total revision of philosophies and religions. Teilhard was annealed by it : traditions, illusions, dogmas and " bright ideas " were shrivelled ; and the basic convictions which took their place had to be compared with· previous professions and beliefs.[2] How far did the pre-war framework of civilisation and of Christendom any longer fit the naked facts ? Or to put it as he did in his *La Vie cosmique* of 1916, " Is it necessary for union with Christ to renounce the journey proper to this cruel world ? We cannot make the surrender of all the charm and nobility of the natural life the condition for beginning the supernatural." Teilhard's reaction was evident and threefold.

[1] For a vivid account see the description of his heroism by his friend Count Max Bégouen in Corte, *La Vie*, pp. 40–2, by Dr. E. Salzes with whom he served (*Nouvelles Lettres*, pp. 17–19) and his own *Nostalgie du front* quoted in *Letters from a Traveller*, p. 50. The recognition of it was marked by his Croix de Guerre in 1915, his Médaille militaire in 1917 and his nomination by his regiment as Chevalier of the Legion of Honour in 1920. For his refusal of a commission, cf. Cuénot, p. 42.

[2] The fullest material for his reaction to war is found in *Genèse d'une pensée* (Grosset, 1961), the letters from Teilhard during the war to his cousin Marguerite Teillard-Chambon (Claude Aragonnès) who had also collected and published his *Lettres de voyage* and *Nouvelles Lettres* and before her death prepared this third volume.

First his philosophy had been purged of its easy dualisms ; for he had seen mankind under conditions to which the old categories, body and soul, good and bad, cannot be readily applied, and seen the universe alike in its unimaginable horror and its transcendent beauty. He had found the presence of unity in diversity not as a problem or an aspiration but as a fact—a fact that challenges the current notions of God and man and the world.[1] So he began to write tentative papers dealing with the new ideas of the cosmos, of becoming and evolution, of the coinherence of multiplicity in the rhythmic pattern of the whole. And these in 1919 he sent by invitation to Blondel for his advice and criticism.[2] These prepared the way for *Le Milieu divin*.

It is in this phase of his growth as George Vass [3] has shown that Blondel's influence upon him is most clearly seen. For most of us life appears as mainly static. During it we perform certain activities rising from simple daily tasks to occasional decisive outbreaks, and we endure as best we can what comes to us of frustration or suffering. So our conduct is fixed and our characters trained. But to Blondel action is the very stuff of existence. We are involved in movement continuously, working or at rest—" they also serve who only stand and wait "—and often to wait is the hardest and most disciplining form of deed. We may separate our lives into outward and inward, activities and passivities. Action not only " fortifies and extends human existence " ; it " makes the world more human " and " is the source of its further evolution ". For by it we are involved in the whole process of divine immanence, we " draw the elements of our environment into our action " [4] and so promote the integration and divinisation of

---

[1] Cf. E. Bréhier, *Transformation*, p. 118.

[2] Cf. Cuénot, p. 55.   [3] In *The Heythrop Journal*, July 1961.

[4] L.c. p. 242, cf. C. d'Armagnac, "De Blondel à Teilhard", *Archives de Philosophie* (1958), pp. 298–312, who argues that though Blondel's estimate of science as solely objective seems to contradict Teilhard's view of its importance for philosophy, yet Teilhard's insistence upon " the within " brings them into agreement.

the whole. Each of us consciously and by our choices and initiative in individual separation yet within the body of Christ builds up the pleroma that is to be.

Teilhard himself stated [1] that Blondel's concept of Action had suggested to him an " exploratory Energy of the biological capacities of evolution " and also the idea of Pan-Christism which he was to develop so richly in his latest works. These between them gave him a sense of the element of design and direction in the creative process not in terms of an external *deus ex machina*, the watchmaker and the watch, but as an inherent quality of the basic stuff of the universe ; a design of which for us men the blue-print was presented to us in Jesus Christ, a direction expressed in the primal energy and its activities and culminating when the cosmogenesis disclosed itself as a Christification. Such is an outline of the Christian philosophy which he and his friends built upon the best science, cosmic, geological and biological, and the best theology, creative, redemptive and inspirational, of their day. This was henceforth his message.

In philosophy Teilhard's upbringing had been appropriate. Light has been thrown on its details by the recent publication of another volume from the writings and letters of his friend and contemporary Auguste Valensin. The two were trained together in Jersey and at Ore ; and the first part of the new book gives continuous reference to the teaching, books and friends that influenced them. The list of names given by Cuénot (p. 19) is supplemented ; the details of the course in philosophy can be collected, and the general impression that the period was not one of much intellectual distinction is on the whole confirmed. But Jules Lebreton, the future author of the important *Origines du dogme de la Trinité*, was a senior student in Jersey, and L. de Grandmaison, whom Teilhard

---

[1] Cf. letter of 15th February 1955 in Cuénot, p. 56. He had previously stated that he saw his own teaching as a " theory of Energy directly affiliated to Blondel's metaphysic of Action " : cf. d'Armagnac, l.c.

called " the divine Léonce ",[1] was a professor at Ore—Lebreton a Scholastic and Thomist, Grandmaison an open-minded but not unorthodox humanist, who kept in touch with Teilhard during the war years. At that time Grandmaison was compiling his *Impressions de guerre de prêtres-soldats*, published in 1916, and editing the review *Études* : Teilhard sent to him certain of his war-time writings which Grandmaison read and praised, but did not publish.

There is little evidence of the strictly theological preparation that Teilhard received. In his training, biblical studies were devotional rather than critical : exegesis was determined on doctrinal and authoritarian lines, and the problems raised by Loisy and others were dismissed unheard. The letters in *Genèse* give no sign of the remarkable understanding of St. Paul which soon became characteristic and dominant for his whole presentation of the Faith. No doubt, as we have seen, this owed something to Blondel's Pan-Christism ; but Father C. C. Martindale,[2] a close friend of Teilhard, ascribed it to the two volumes of Fernand Prat the Jesuit scholar on *Théologie de saint Paul*, first published in 1921 and translated into English in 1945.

Of the social application of Christianity with which Teilhard was deeply concerned in his later years there is little sign in his training. At Ore, H. de Genouillac expounded the method and ideas of Durkheim,[3] and Teilhard studied the world of Henri de Tourville, one of the great Le Play's first disciples in the School of Social Science ; and this last seems to have had a permanent influence on the development of his humanitarian and reforming activities.[4]

The second phase of his reaction to his now matured experience inevitably concerned his own individual place in the process which he was thus beginning to visualise. He had been ordained to the priesthood of the Catholic Church and

[1] Cf. Cuénot, p. 26.
[2] In a letter to me of May 1961.
[3] Cf. *A. Valensin, textes et documents*, p. 55.   [4] *Genèse*, p. 159.

was a member of the Society of Jesus.[1] How could the special conditions of this twofold loyalty be regarded as promoting or restricting his work ? He had grown up in the atmosphere and under the guidance of a strict discipline in which obedience played a fundamental part. He had pledged himself and been admitted to a status which cut him off from much of life and committed him to particular duties and renunciations. Yet he had seen in war the paradox of men whose orthodoxy appeared to give them none of the supreme qualities of love and mercy, endurance and self-sacrifice, and of men for whom God was meaningless and Christ a mockery, and who yet disclosed in moments of effort and agony a radiance and hero-ism beyond normal manhood. To this fact he could never be false : of it he could never be forgetful.

Yet even when his Society acquiesced in his exile and his Church forbade the publication of his books or the acceptance of public opportunities, even when his friends urged him to follow the way of Loisy [2] and others who could not consent to conceal their convictions, he still insisted upon maintaining his obligations and urging that the conditions under which he had come to his experience were those to be observed in its fulfilment. That he had a sense of humour, a ready wit and sometimes an indiscreet tongue may be admitted : but only on the rarest occasions and to intimate friends like Father Bergounioux [3] did he disclose how deep was the suffering and how hard the struggle against embitterment.

At the time of his post-war settlements his thoughts on his own mission centred upon priesthood, sacramentalism and evangelism—upon his self-discipline, his ministry and his message. The writings that best disclose his decisions are *Le Prêtre* (1918) written at the time when he took his vows and

[1] His interpretation of his vocation is nobly expressed in *Le Prêtre* written in 1918 and quoted by the editors in *Genèse*, p. 14.

[2] Cuénot, p. 149 n.

[3] L.c. p. 447. Add to this the testimony of Paul Rivet in *Réflexion sur le bonheur*, pp. 139–42.

quoted at some length by Dr. Cuénot,[1] *La Messe sur le monde* (1923), written on his journey from Peking to Ordos with Licent, and *Le Milieu divin* (1926-27), published in English 1960. In the first of these he develops his view that his work as a priest is also that of an apostle and evangelist proclaiming by thought, word and deed the unity of all men in a milieu "divinised" by the Incarnation, "divinising" by the Communion, "*divinisable*" by our co-operation. It would seem that in the trenches he had concentrated upon the great Pauline gospel expounded in his later Epistles. Like St. Paul he was aiming at the goal of a universal Christendom, the *plérome* as he constantly calls it of the Christ. But like him also he was content to be an Apostle to the Gentiles[2]—to speak principally to those outside the Church, and particularly to his fellow-scientists. There is abundant evidence of the influence upon them and upon laity in general both of his addresses and his writings.[3]

But in fulfilling it trouble was inevitable. In 1921 he had delivered a paper at the Institut Catholique on the Present State of the question of Transformism,[4] which Cuénot treats as a piece of pioneering. Certainly the whole subject of Evolution had been boycotted in Church circles[5] and on this occasion it led to a violent outcry on the subject of Original Sin. The controversy led to the exclusion of Teilhard from the Institut[6] and to his virtual banishment to China in 1926 : in spite of the loyal support of his friends and his own repeated evidence of his obedience and devotion, the author of *La Messe sur le monde* and *Le Milieu divin* remained from thenceforth under a cloud, insecure as to his position and given no opportunity either to meet his accusers or to plead his cause

[1] L.c. pp. 43-4, 56-8.
[2] L.c. p. 85.
[3] For striking examples cf., e.g., Cuénot, pp. 82-3.
[4] Printed in *La Vision du passé* (Vol. 3, of Teilhard's works), pp. 17-40.
[5] No papal pronouncement even mentioned it until the Encyclical *Humani Generis* in 1950, ninety years after the *Origin of Species*.
[6] Cf. Cuénot, p. 85.

with Catholic authority. Only the evidence of his intimates and an occasional reference in letters indicate how much the slur upon his ministry, the suppression of his convictions, and the banishment from his intellectual and religious home involved for him.

So arose the third element in his response to his life's work, his professional training as palaeontologist. As a child his interest had been in natural history, " the works of creation " as John Ray called it. He had the open eyes and the dis-criminating curiosity of those for whom the study of life in all its forms is a chief delight, and who cheerfully follow the first of Adam's tasks, the giving names to all other creatures. But Teilhard was much more than a collector of flora and fauna : he was as Cuénot has called him a " son of Demeter " to whom earth itself, its shape and structure and stratification, was not only an experience to be enjoyed, but a neighbour-hood to be explored and a mystery to be investigated. Un-like many naturalists he had inherited a sense of the relationship between the organism and its environment which has now become characteristic of medical and biological research. From the study of rocks to that of fossils and so to the records of evolution and of human origins had been his development during his boyhood in Auvergne and Jersey, his youth in Egypt and at Hastings and his maturity in the Museum of Natural History in Paris where after the war he settled down under the supervision of Marcellin Boule and the assistance of Abbé Henri Breuil.

Teilhard had, as Corte recognises,[1] in his early paper on " Prehistory and its development " (*Études*, t. 134, pp. 40–53, January 1913) given clear evidence that he regarded human origins as the battle-front—a fact in keeping with the Dar-winian controversy when *The Origin of Species* aroused less emotional conflict than *The Descent of Man*. So as soon as his work on the carnivorous mammals from Quercy had been expanded into his doctor's thesis on the French mammals of

[1] *La Vie et l'âme de Teilhard*, p. 47.

the Lower Eocene by his field-work in the neighbourhood of
Rheims in 1922, he received a chair of geology at the Institut
and devoted himself to expounding the work of Boule on
fossil men [1] and insisting that religion must face this new
knowledge since " Faith has need of all the truth ".

It was in the laboratory of the Museum of Natural History
in Paris that Teilhard got his full and expert knowledge of
early man. Marcellin Boule, Professor there since 1902 and
himself from the Auvergne, was the scientist at that time best
qualified to teach him : for though he undertook several
expeditions to America and parts of Africa, he was more a
man of museums than of field-work and had the collector's
passion for exact taxonomy and a massive knowledge of the
literature and the achievements of contemporary anthropology
and of all the principle Western centres of early human habita-
tion. His career had been from its beginning devoted to
geology, palaeontology and anthropology, and having gained
his licentiate in his twenty-third year he moved to Paris and
became attached to the department of palaeontology at the
Museum where he celebrated his jubilee in 1937, five years
before his death. More than any other he opened up our
understanding of the evolution, organisation, convergence and
variation of our human ancestors, and Teilhard's debt to him
in this field is greater than to any other. He and all the rest
of us owe to Boule not only our knowledge of the life and
works of primitive man, but the creation of centres for anthropological research, the gathering and classification of great
masses of material, and the first statement of a real natural
history of humanity. His energy which influenced the whole
development of palaeontology, his authority often almost dic-
tatorial in its commands, his enthusiasm which Teilhard on
occasion found himself almost bound to resist, and with it all
his human qualities of mind and heart gave him not only his
leadership but his power of co-operation. If Teilhard got from
Le Roy and Blondel his understanding of philosophy and

[1] Reprinted in *L'Apparition de l'homme*, pp. 41-50.

religion, it was to Boule that he owed his scientific stature, his mastery of method, his power of exact definition and his sound judgment.

In Boule's laboratory he was brought into close touch with Henri Breuil,[1] then a student four years older than himself but destined to become the "pope of anthropology". He had been educated in Paris at the Sorbonne and the Catholic Institute, and after five years in Switzerland had been working since 1910 at the Institute of Human Palaeontology, and became professor at the Collège de France from 1929–47. Of his early life, his passion for nature stimulated by his father's collection of insects, of the schoolmasters who interested him in geology and the Stone Age, and of his drawings of beasts and flowers and in his seminarist days his copying of the frescoes in the Reindeer Age caves he has left us a charming account in the introduction to his picture-book *Beyond the Bounds of History*.[2] To this Field-Marshal Smuts contributed a Foreword written a year before his death in which he confessed that when he looked at history he " was tempted to be a pessimist about man ". " But when I look at prehistory I am an optimist. The case for progress on the evidence of prehistory is simply overwhelming. For us, children of to-day, prehistory is a message—a call to good cheer and faith in our future." [3] Teilhard's optimism, for which theologians have so often rebuked him, must have drawn some of its courage from that same source.

To what extent Breuil's religion helped Teilhard towards his own synthesis is not easy to discover. His interest in the art and culture of primitive man, in his paintings and hunting and craftsmanship, made the problem of evolution less urgent for him than for Teilhard ; he was more of a historian than of a physiologist, as much an artist as a scientist. But if Teilhard's mind gained more from Le Roy and Blondel, and his palaeontology more from Boule, Breuil's friendliness,

---

[1] There is an excellent comparison of the three men in Cuénot, pp. 217–218.   [2] Published by Gawthorn, 1949.   [3] L.c. p. 9.

happiness and charm and his visits to China must have been invaluable to him, and their priesthood gave them something unique in common.

It was after the publication in 1929 along with Yang, C. C. of his first paper on Chou-Kou-Tien and the finding of Sinanthropus [1] and of his more general essay *What are we to think of transformism?* [2] in January 1930 that Teilhard's reconciliation of his palaeontological work on human origins and his theological concept of the cosmic Christ as the consummation of the evolutionary process was fully accomplished and the idea of the *Phenomenon of Man* became clear to him. The treatise on transformism was directed partly to the Catholics, particularly in New York, who regarded evolution as synonymous with materialism and partly to the scientists who refused to estimate it by the fullness of its achievement in humanity and the manhood of Christ. It consisted of a statement of five principles which should be accepted about it, and itself concluded with two great sayings, first to scientists, " Transformism does not necessarily open the doors to an invasion of Spirit by Matter : rather it witnesses in favour of the essential triumph of Spirit. Moreover, if not better than Fixism, Evolutionism can give to the Universe the grandeur, profundity and unity which are the natural atmosphere of the Christian faith " ; and then to his fellow-Christians, " The world will never be so vast nor humanity ever so strong as to be worthy of Him who has created them and is incarnate in them." [3]

[1] *Bulletin of the Geological Society of China*, VIII, 3.
[2] *Revue des Questions Scientifiques*, XVII, 1, reprinted in *La Vision du passé*, pp. 213–23.
[3] As evidence of the depth and insight of Teilhard's Catholicism of the interesting comparison between his basic outlook and convictions and those of Dante in Miss B. Reynold's recent introduction to the Paradiso of *The Divine Comedy*, iii, pp. 29–34 (Penguin Classics, 1962).

CHAPTER THREE

TEILHARD IN BRITAIN

IT WAS ON THE FIRST OCCASION on which I had an opportunity of discussing Teilhard with his younger colleague and close companion, the Jesuit biologist and geneticist Pierre Leroy, that I got confirmation of the conviction that England had counted for more in his life than had been recognised. It was obvious to anyone who had known evolutionary speculation in Britain in the second and third decades of this century when William Bateson had recovered the researches of Mendel, when the Mendel-de Vries theory was providing an alternative to orthodox Darwinism and when support of Lamarckianism was shaken by the suicide of Kammerer, that Teilhard was very close in the general character of his philosophy and in particular details of its exposition to the new school, whose watchword was emergence and who took it for granted that continuity of process must be so interpreted as to leave full room for the arrival of the new and unpredictable.

Father Leroy, as soon as he realised that I was English and Teilhardian, said at once that he had come to be sure that his four years in England had played a large part in his friend's development. Looking into the matter it seemed at once evident that these years, and especially 1910–11, were for him a time of rapid emotional as well as intellectual growth. On his own evidence, given in *Le Cœur de la matière* [1] and else-

---

[1] The detailed account as recorded by him is given below in Chapter Five.

where, he had matured slowly. It was only as the period of his ordination approached that his whole self had suddenly expanded and he came fully of age.[1] Certainly his innate love of nature and powers of wonder and appreciation had then been directed towards specific palaeontological problems and brought to public notice when he was at the Jesuit College at Ore Place near Hastings, doing his four years of theological training. Geology and fossil-hunting had attracted him in his first stage of work in Jersey and then more intensively in Egypt, but this was only a part of his general interest in natural history and he was in no sense an expert in palaeontology or as yet a believer in evolution. The origin of man was outside his concern. At Ore he found an inseparable companion among his fellow-students, Félix Pelletier, who was a chemist and mineralogist, had been with him in Jersey, and had joined with him in 1904 in contributing a paper on the geology of the Isle to the annual bulletin of the Jersey Society. At Hastings the two men used their scanty leisure to explore the Wealden sandstone quarries in the neighbourhood and the Fairlight clay just to the east of Ore Place. In the Ashdown Sand there Teilhard discovered the tooth of a new species of small mammal, *Dipriodon valdensis*;[2] and we have a striking testimony to their energy and discrimination in a paper by Professor A. C. Seward of Cambridge on the fossil plants which they had collected for Charles Dawson the Lewes solicitor and geologist and which he had presented for them to the British Museum in November 1911. All of these came from Fairlight and one tiny branchlet found by Teilhard was a new species and was named *Lycopoditis teilhardi*. Seward's paper was read to the Geological Society of London on 6th November 1912,[3] and in the discussion Dawson spoke

[1] This is specially stated in the "Clausule" on pp. 33-4 of *Le Cœur*, where he deals with the significance of sex.

[2] Reported by A. Smith Woodward in *Quarterly Journal of the Geological Society*, 67, p. 279, 22nd March 1911.

[3] Printed in the *Quarterly Journal*, 69, p. 86, plate XI 2a and b, 2.

warmly of their skill and of the collections that they had presented to London and Hastings. He had met them apparently in 1909 in consequence of a report from workmen at the locality whom he paid to save fossils for him; but he was already concerned with his finds at Piltdown gravel-beds near Uckfield; and through him Teilhard became connected with the work there.

Dawson had noticed the pits many years before, possibly in 1898, had asked the gravel-diggers to keep a look-out for fossils, and had received from them as he claimed a piece of what he thought to be a human parietal bone. In the paper in which he eventually reported the whole story he says nothing about the men having found a large round bone which they thought was a coconut and smashed up [1]—a dramatic tale which Sir Alfred Smith Woodward the eminent geologist related at length in his book *The Earliest Englishman*, written just before his death in 1944 and published in The Thinker's Library in 1948. It was " some years later in the autumn of 1911 " that Dawson found a larger bit containing part of the left superciliary ridge, and on 24th May 1912 took this up to Woodward, then Keeper of the department at the British Museum of Natural History, who inspected the bone, declared it to be ancient, and decided that a thorough search of the locality must be undertaken.

Early in the year the beds were flooded. But as soon as they dried up the two men with an elderly labourer and apparently Teilhard [2] began their exploration on 2nd June with the sanction and support of the landowner and the farmer. Various pieces fitting on to those already found made up a fairly complete brain-case. Then when it seemed that further

[1] Dawson printed a fuller account in the *Hastings and East Sussex Naturalist*, vol. 2, No. 2, 1913, pp. 73–82 ; No. 4, 1915, pp. 182–4 ; No. 6, 1917, pp. 251–3.

[2] See J. S. Weiner, *The Piltdown Forgery*, p. 88, quoting a letter from Dawson to Woodward. This book is a detailed, thorough and judicious account of the whole episode.

search was useless Dawson suddenly scooped up the left half of a lower jaw with two molars still in place but the point and the front teeth broken off. It seems to have been after this that Woodward suggested that they bring in the two young students from Ore Place ; and as Dawson said in a footnote,[1] " Father P. Teilhard, S.J., who accompanied us on one occasion discovered one of the implements in situ " and a bit of elephant's tooth : but nothing more was found ; and the two Jesuits left Ore having finished their theological training.

Dawson and Woodward then submitted a double paper to the Society—Dawson reporting the finding of the fragments in some detail and Woodward describing their characteristics and importance. This was read on 18th December 1912,[2] and in the discussion D. Waterston, Professor of Human Anatomy at the Middlesex Hospital, bluntly stated that skull and jaw could not belong to the same individual or perhaps even to the same species, since the jaw was much more simian and in any case did not fit the upper bones. C. W. Andrews, Woodward's colleague, and perhaps M. A. C. Hinton of the Zoological Department shared this view but could not be persuaded to speak publicly about it. Marcellin Boule, and afterwards Franz Weidenreich and several others of Teilhard's friends, were also convinced that skull and lower jaw did not belong together.

So far Teilhard had hardly touched the event. In any case he was then only a beginner and was always very modest and silent in the presence of his seniors. But next year he became fully involved. A supplementary paper read by Dawson in the winter of 1913 [3] told of a further discovery. On 30th August 1913 [4] Teilhard who " had worked with them for

[1] *Quarterly Journal*, 69, p. 122. These two finds and indeed all the Piltdown fossils are now proved to have been stained and faked.

[2] *Quarterly Journal*, 69, pp. 117–24.

[3] *Quarterly Journal*, 70, pp. 86–92.

[4] Cuénot, p. 37, speaks of the visit to England during which Teilhard went to Ore and Lewes and Piltdown as starting at the end of July.

three days " had found a left canine tooth at the same place as that on which the jaw had been dug up—and the two seemed to fit. Woodward gave details telling how Teilhard had been doing heavy work on a trench, how Woodward had taken his place and put him on to sift the spoil-heap, and how he had suddenly told them of his find. According to Teilhard's friends it was a thrilling moment which he never forgot ; he was a young man working with experts and this was a clinching proof of the antiquity and significance of this veritable missing link ; and he, the then unknown French student, had now a real share in it. Dawson also reported his own find of nasal bones apparently belonging to the same skull.

The story was completed after Dawson's death in 1916 when Woodward read a final paper describing Dawson's subsequent finds of pieces of a similar skull and mandible in a field two miles away [1] and a large bit of worked elephant bone.

Undoubtedly this episode, slight as was his connection with it, made a deep impression upon Teilhard. Clearly and long before the exposure of the fraud he had become highly suspicious of it—partly because the opinion of Boule and of other experts shook his acceptance of the find as genuine, but still more because as he became familiar with the primitive sites of human and quasi-human origins, it became impossible to think of Britain or indeed Europe as the birthplace of mankind. Whenever the subject was discussed (and its effect upon palaeontology made discussion inevitable), he always described it as a riddle and refused to speculate upon its author. When in 1953 he heard of Dr. Kenneth P. Oakley's un-answerable demonstration of the faking of the whole evidence he was quick to send his congratulations and express his re-lief —though he felt bound to say, " I am fundamentally convinced of your conclusions—but all the same speaking

---

[1] *Quarterly Journal*, 73, pp. 1–8. Dawson had reported this to Wood-ward in 1915 but the actual date of the discovery is unknown.

sentimentally it spoils one of the clearest and oldest of my palaeontological memories." Yet he stated " anatomically speaking Eoanthropus was a sort of monster ; and for palaeontology
it was equally absurd to suppose that in the dawn of mankind
a man could appear in England." [1] He specifically refused to
believe that Dawson was personally to blame or that Sir
Arthur could have been a party to it : [2] according to Corte [3]
he even said that he felt that Dawson himself must have
been duped. It is evident, both from the history of the
work at Piltdown and from his own attitude then and
afterwards, that he had no personal knowledge of the
fraud.

Since the original disclosure of the forgery in 1953 further
evidence as to the dating and possible provenance of the bones
has been supplied in a joint paper by Professor H. de Vries of
Groningen who submitted them to a thorough testing by the
latest radio-carbon method and Dr. Oakley who commented
in detail on the results.[4] The tests proved that both bones
were " antique-modern " the human skull 620±100 years
" less than 800 years old ", the orang jaw more recent, 500
±100, "possibly several centuries old". The skull is a thick-
boned specimen such as could be found in any ancient
burial-ground. But Oakley brings forward some very
interesting evidence as to the origin of the jaw. The dyaks
of Borneo are known to have kept orang skulls as fetishes
and he prints a photograph by Mr. Tom Harrisson of such a
skull with jaw, kept in a " long house " and said to be twenty
generations old. And A. H. Everett is known to have brought
home a collection of such skulls, one at least a trophy, many
of which were presented to the British Museum. One of

[1] Letter of 28th November 1953.
[2] So did Dr. Barbour who knew the Woodwards well, and had discussed
the whole matter with Teilhard after the exposure.
[3] *La Vie et l'âme*, p. 39, a letter quoted in *L'Apparition de l'homme*,
p. 17.
[4] *Nature*, vol. 184, pp. 224-6, July 1959.

these shows a close resemblance in nitrogen content to the Piltdown jaw. The relevant material for the deception could thus have been accessible in England—though it is wise to follow Dr. Oakley's example and draw no more specific inferences.

The elaborate and highly skilful fraud with which the evidence was prepared and planted is indisputable ; the place and people concerned in it were well known ; the mystery should surely be easy to penetrate. Yet even to-day it has never been brought home to its author with any positive proof. It is easy to argue that only one of those known to have been associated with the drama could reasonably be suspected ; and, in spite of Teilhard's refusal to condemn him, Dawson remains the only obvious candidate—with or without a possible accessory or "producer". That seems the proper verdict. But there is one circumstance characteristic of the time which makes it, I think, not quite impossible that the forger was some unknown Englishman in touch with them both and possibly one of Dawson's local enemies.[1] But if so, what was his motive ? Surely the suggestion that it was a practical joke which went too far is hardly adequate.

Those of us then in our early manhood will remember from experience the extraordinary wave of British religious patriotism which was then sweeping over the country. The succession of small wars on the frontiers of empire ; the crises from Fashoda to Agadir ; the jingoism of Elgar and Kipling ; the shock of the "great Boer War" ; the social upheavals of Lloyd Georgian finance ; the break-down of the conspiracy of silence over science and religion ; these presages of a new age were accompanied by an unprecedented out-break of religious fantasy and fiction. Beliefs and legends supported by fakes far less plausible than Eoanthropus were accepted and proclaimed by people of good standing and normal education from Tunbridge Wells and St. Leonards to

[1] Weiner gives an account of several though without establishing any clear suspicion, l.c. pp. 154-68.

Cheltenham and Bath. That the Hebrew tribe of Dan had migrated north and west and become the people of Britain was proved by linguistic evidence—Danai among the early Greeks, Danube the river whose course they followed, Denmark and our Danish invaders ; so the wandering Jews had brought with them for their English offspring the blessings appropriated by the prophets to the people of God. Alternatively the house of Windsor was directly descended from the house of David, the genealogy fully compiled till the fall of Jerusalem, then passing by way of Egypt and North Africa to a legendary ancestor of the Irish kings, and so obscurely and with variants to the line of Tudor and to our present sovereign who was thus the lawful heir and owner of the prerogatives of Davidic descent. These and similar legends supported by the precise calculation of the day and year of the Second Advent derived from the cryptograms of the book of Daniel and the measurements of the passages in the Great Pyramid and fixing a series of dates between 1907 and 1923, crude parodies of the mythology of " British Israel ", carried conviction to Empire-builders and biblical enthusiasts. If it was a legitimate duty to transfer the world-dominion of Israel to Britain on such evidence, then it would be a step in the same direction to transfer Eden itself to " England's green and pleasant land " : Adam's ancestors must surely have lived in Sussex.[1]

For Teilhard, whenever his first doubts began, the experience fixed his primary interest. Thenceforth, though in August 1911 he had been ordained into the priesthood and in 1918 had taken the three vows of poverty, chastity and obedience, he continued to work also as a palaeontologist. Already in June 1913, very soon after finishing his theological training at Ore Place, he was studying under Boule in Paris and joined a party under Hugo Obermaier, of which Nels C.

---

[1] If this suggestion seems irrelevant, attention may be drawn to Weiner's detailed examination of possible motives *Piltdown Forgery*, pp. 117–19. For a parallel cf. note at end of chapter.

Nelson of the Museum of Natural History, New York, the Abbé Henri Breuil and Miles Burkitt were also members, to visit Altamira and the cave of Castillo in North-west Spain.[1] He had thus acquired a considerable experience of palaeontology before the outbreak of the First World War, and his five years of service as a stretcher-bearer on the Western front.

Before we pass from this, his only continuous stay in England, one point on which his future work may be regarded as open to criticism and which is certainly of interest to British readers may be mentioned. His contact with scientists here was as yet limited to geologists and hardly affected the general problems of evolutionary biology. Otherwise, especially at that time, his acquaintance with us must have made him familiar with the widespread interest in genetics and the controversies then so violently waged between the orthodox Darwinians with their insistence upon small variations sifted, fixed and developed by natural selection, and the Mendelians with their study of the physiology of heredity and of the fact and importance of mutations. Great progress had been made in the verification of Mendel's original theory, of the extent and possible limitations of its applicability, and of the mechanisms by which its results were achieved. It seemed, and still to some extent seems, that if we could discover the basic causes which originate change this would put us on the way to a full understanding of the creative process. To-day we have realised that much of the talk about randomness is only a confession of our ignorance, that an adequate explanation of the incidence and the scale of these apparent breaks in the orderly sequence of development is still beyond our knowledge ; and that study of life at the molecular level is giving us a new approach to the subject. But in the years when Teilhard was in Sussex the controversy of which Professors E. B. Poulton and W. Bateson were the protagonists convulsed the biological world.

[1] Cf. M. Burkitt, *The Old Stone Age*, pp. 19–24, etc.

Teilhard himself accepted and insisted upon the fact of novelty in evolution and came to use the word " emergence " in its technical sense : but he always seems to have regarded progress as slow in detail even though attaining at certain points new and unpredictable levels of attainment. If he had realised the scientific probability of the jumps which tradition tended to deny,[1] he would have found it easier to avoid the long discussion of the apparent absence of true intermediates. He might also have dealt more fully with those seemingly great gaps in continuity for which Professor A. M. Dalcq of Brussels has formed his theory of onto-mutations.[2]

Indeed, while at Ore Teilhard does not seem to have read many English books, though in 1910 he was attracted by the Catholic novels of R. H. Benson and especially by *The Light Invisible*. This so impressed him that in the autumn of 1916 he wrote three tales in a similar style which Grandmaison would not accept for *Études*. Later when he read *Lord of the World* in 1918 he recognised how much he disliked Benson's attitude towards this mundane sphere. To the novelist all concern with worldly interests was of Antichrist ; to Teilhard such a verdict seemed " unjust, bloodless and anti-natural ", the sort of outlook which he had now learned to think unworthy of the Creator or of the Christ.[3]

In the years of war Teilhard had no direct contact with Britain. Though his service took him from Nieuport and Ypres to Arras and the Chemin des Dames as well as to the battles at Verdun and the borders of Alsace, there is no record of contact with British armies or individuals. But before his discharge, when he was free to read and think and was in fact discovering and defining the faith which had been tested and enlarged by his new experience, he describes at some length the impact which the books of R. H. Benson, H. G.

[1] Cf. " *Natura nihil facit per saltum* ".
[2] Cf. articles by him in *Ann. Soc. Roy. de Zoologie*, 82, pp. 117-38, and in *Bull. Soc. Zool. de France*, 7, pp. 240-55.
[3] Cf. *Genèse*, pp. 305-8.

Wells and Rudyard Kipling made upon him.[1] For Benson, whom he had already read, he lost his first enthusiasm. But Wells, though he realised the errors of his theology and his misrepresentations of Catholicism, attracted and surprised him. He found in *God the Invisible King* a strong and unexpected sense of the linkage of the human individual with the community, a "*mystique de l'Effort humain*" which gave the book the sincerity of an appeal to the *immédiateté* of the divine. This saves Wells from dilettantism and qualifies him as "a lifelong seeker for truth". "Have we", Teilhard asks, "a single novelist like this in France?" After a comparison with Benson, whom he now condemns, he claims that Kipling in all the range of his work and particularly in *The Light that Failed* showed the same universality and recognition of the worth of human effort. Like William James, whose great book he mentions in this connection, they have little insight into the true inwardness of religion : this is "*une lacune anglo-saxonne*" : but does not destroy the value and significance of their practical and humane interests !

In August 1920 he spent a month in Jersey with R. R. Marett, and then a few days in London. In 1921 his thesis was duly presented on 5th July and the award of a doctorate at the Sorbonne with the degree of *très honorable* was duly made on 22nd March 1922. In September he visited Niaux with Breuil and Miss Dorothy Garrod, who was working with Professor W. J. Sollas at Oxford, and with whom he kept in touch at irregular intervals. She was a Roman Catholic but not wholly free from problems and uncertainties on which he was able to help her, particularly by the script of *Le Milieu divin* when he met her again in 1925.[2] In June 1923 a joint paper by him and his friend Dr. Louis Dollo, Director of the Royal

---

[1] Cf. *Genèse*, pp. 353–65, letters of 1st, 8th and 14th January 1919 from Strasbourg. In these Teilhard finds himself entirely on their side. It foreshadows the Anglophil tendencies which, as Dr. Cuénot demonstrates, became so strong in his later years.

[2] Cuénot, pp. 47, 79, 82.

Museum in Brussels, was read before the Geological Society of London and printed in its *Quarterly Journal*, vol. 80, pp. 12–16, on the fossil mammals of Belgium.

This was after his departure for China when he joined Père Licent at Tientsin in 1923–24 and discovered early human remains at Ordos far west of Peking. He came back to France in November, and in April 1925 visited Britain and went to the Natural History Museum where he met Dr. A. Tindell Hopwood, then working there on the fossil mammals, who became his friend at once. Then with Breuil and Miss Garrod he visited the museum in Ipswich and explored the Red and Coralline Crag where Mr J. Reid Moir had found laurel and leaf flint blades which Breuil regarded as Solutrean.[1] The next week they examined the glacial and interglacial cliffs at Cromer. Their purpose was to study the character and if possible determine the date of these chipped stones, most of which are now regarded as eoliths and of natural origin, but which were then claimed by some to be artifacts of Palaeolithic origin. On this occasion Teilhard met a number of British anthropologists, but did not apparently feel very satisfied as to the existence in this area of human relics of great antiquity. His own work in China was giving him a sense of the importance of Asia which made the claims of Europe seem unsound.

After this it was a long time before he came back to Britain. The exploration of Chou-Kou-Tien, the adventure of the Yellow Cruise, and von Koenigswald's opening up of the fossil-beds of Java kept his attention focused on the East as the probable cradle of mankind. Like his friends he had never been wholly convinced by Eoanthropus and the Piltdown finds ;

[1] Cf. D. A. E. Garrod, *The Upper Palaeolithic Age in Britain*, p. 170.

J. Reid Moir's book, *The Antiquity of Man in East Anglia* (Cambridge, 1927), is a detailed account of his finds in Ipswich and Eastern England, an attempt to prove their early date, and a claim that in spite of Pithecanthropus East Anglia may be the home of the first man. He was, of course, encouraged by the verdict of Woodward, Keith and Ray Lankester on the Piltdown skull.

and each year confirmed what the African discoveries were to corroborate, that the crucial changes from ape to man took place on or near the tropics of the Eastern hemisphere.

In fact, though he did much travel between 1925 and 1937 he does not seem to have thought of England until his return from the conference of experts in Philadelphia in 1937 when he had planned to stay [1] for a few days with the Garrods in Wordsworth Grove, Cambridge. This was prevented by illness, but he came over from France in March 1939, visited Cambridge and saw T. T. Paterson, curator of the museum of Ethnology,[2] Miles Burkitt and a few others. He was in England for a week mainly to consult Paterson about a projected expedition to India.

A further and somewhat different approach to Britain arose through, and is described by his friend of the Institute of Anthropology in Paris, Jacques Bacot,[3] the Orientalist, and a connection of Teilhard by marriage. Bacot describes how at a time when the Institute and anthropologists generally were strongly materialistic in outlook, they nevertheless rejoiced in Teilhard's appearance among them and at the knowledge that a Jesuit was interested in their work. At these gatherings his old teacher, Marcellin Boule, and his friend of war-time, Paul Rivet, and others who afterwards supported him for the professorship of the Collège de France came to appreciate not only his knowledge and ability but his gaiety and modesty and vitalising influence. Bacot was at this time closely connected with the French branch of the World Congress of Faiths, the movement started in England in the twenties by Sir Francis Younghusband who had been head of an expedition to Lhasa in 1904 and who in his last years devoted himself to the founding and establishment of the Congress. He had

[1] Cf. Cuénot, pp. 181, 273.
[2] Now in the Department of Social Anthropology, University of Glasgow.
[3] Cf. his paper in Cahier 2, *Réflexions sur le bonheur*, pp. 143–9, and Cuénot, p. 357.

visited Paris for a conference in 1939 : and after his death Lady Ravensdale, Baron Palmstierna and others revived the Congress in London in 1945 and organised a meeting of the French branch in the Institute of Anthropology in Paris early in 1947. To this Bacot invited Teilhard on his return from China ; and to it he read the paper *La Foi en l'homme* circulated in typescript in February of that year. At the Congress Teilhard's friend Édouard Le Roy in spite of his ill-health, Étienne Gilson the Scholastic and Gabriel Marcel the Existentialist were present and took an active part in the discussion ; and this according to Bacot did much to revive the branch and to enlarge Teilhard's contacts with Britain.

Early in that same year Teilhard received an invitation from Field-Marshal Smuts, who was then Prime Minister of South Africa, to visit and study the rich collections of fossils, particularly of Australopithecus recently found in Sterkfontein and Makapan. This proposal came at the instigation of Abbé Breuil who had been in Africa since 1942 ; plans were made for July, but Teilhard was prevented from sailing by a sudden coronary thrombosis. His friend Professor George Barbour, the geologist with whom he had worked in China, went to Africa without him : but Smuts died before Teilhard was able to travel, and the two men never had the opportunity to meet.

There is in Dr. Cuénot's " Life " little detailed evidence of subsequent contacts like those in 1951 and 1954 with his fellow-palaeontologists or friends in England. It is therefore of interest to know of his presence in August 1948, after attending a conference on Eastern and Western Mysticism on 4th July in Paris, at the 18th International Geological Congress in London.[1] In connection with this he joined the excursion planned for the fortnight 2nd to 16th September which visited the most important sites for the study of fossil fish and covered a wide range from South Wales to the extreme north of Scotland. The party left London by road for

[1] A letter dated from Les Moulins 4th September 1948 is in *Letters from a Traveller*, p. 297. I cannot but think that this should be 1949.

Abergavenny. They travelled by Oxford and Gloucester, visited Cementstones Quarry near Mitcheldean in the Forest of Dean and went on by way of Monmouth to the limestone of Onon. Next day they inspected the Breconian brown-stones at Crickhowell, the Dittonian sandstone at Pool Quarry and Castle Mattock, and the Upper Downtonian at Clay Hill. 4th and 5th September were spent at Ludlow exploring the bone-beds and making short excursions to various sandstone and carboniferous centres where a wide range of Silurian freshwater fishes can be studied. On the 6th the party left by the ancient Watling Street to Shrewsbury, Whitchurch, Tar-porley and Warrington and through the Lancashire coalfield to Preston and Lancaster, thence over the Kirkstone to Ulls-water, Penrith and Carlisle. This was a day of travel : they drove some two hundred miles over a revealing sample of the geological structure of England, but it was a study of landscape rather than an opportunity for vertebrate palaeontology.

In Scotland next day they returned to the rocks, moving across the border to the fish-beds of Eskdale, the Permian of the Annandale depression and so to Moffat and Lanark where they visited areas similar to those explored at Ludlow and collected good material around Lesmahagow. On 9th September they travelled from Lanark by way of Airdrie, Stirling, Bridge of Allan and Perth to Forfar where they spent two days exploring the many quarries which had been famous localities for fossils and still yielded good results. On the 11th they went on by Stonehaven, Cowie Bay and Dee-side skirting Lochnagar and the Cairngorms by Rynie, Huntly and Keith to Elgin. There they spent two full days exploring the Old and New Red Sandstones in their study of the Moray fish-beds. In the Guide prepared for the excursion from which this itinerary is taken there are lists of the fifteen quarries and sites between Lossiemouth, the Findhorn, Nairn and Wood-side near Inverness with notes of the fishes found in them. After a night at Inverness they drove on 15th September to Thurso by the Edderton fish-beds, Golspie and Helmsdale to the granite and conglomerate of Caithness where next day various places were explored, among them Achanarras quarry with its very rich fauna. On the 17th the party finished its work and came back by rail to London. They had explored and collected from forty different localities specimens which were packed and distributed to the members of the excursion by Mr. H. A. Toombs of the Natural History Museum who had acted as Secretary to the party. An excellent Guide-book had been prepared for the journey by the leaders, Professor D. M. S. Watson, of University College, T. S. Westoll who supervised the Scottish section and Dr. Errol White with Toombs for England and Wales. Teilhard accompanied it, thoroughly enjoyed the whole journey and made a valuable contribution to its success. Professor Watson, to whom I owe the detail of this adventure, wrote to me that " he was a man of extraordinary mental ability and remarkable personal charm" whose " contacts in England were really of importance to him ".[1]

During these visits he renewed his acquaintance with a number of Englishmen, some of them workers in palaeontology and others members of his Society. In 1950, on 24th May, at the Annual Meeting of the Linnean Society of London, he was elected a Foreign Member,[2] but does not seem to have been able to attend any meetings. In 1951 A. Tindell Hopwood,[3] who had first met him in 1925 and had since published in 1933 a paper on " the Miocene primates of Kenya " and the discovery at Kanam by L. S. B. Leakey in 1932, and in 1951 added a chapter to Leakey's book on Olduvai Gorge, was still working at the Museum and on this occasion was introduced by Teilhard to George Barbour as " one of us ". Father C. C. Martindale, the great Jesuit

[1] Letter of 27th April 1961.
[2] *Proceedings*, vol. 162, p. 189. An Obituary Notice giving a brief but excellent summary and appreciation of his work and character by Dr. Tindell Hopwood is in *Proceedings*, vol. 167, pp. 141–2.
[3] Cf. *Letters from a Traveller*, p. 304, letter of 11th July 1951.

preacher, was also then in London and saw him frequently. He was certainly back in 1954 and may well have been more often in England than has been yet recorded. Both these friends have described their delight in his visits and the effect on them of his vitality, his frank and spontaneous talk, his modesty and sense of wonder and of the " beyond ". He had the capacity to respond at once to their interests and to enjoy exploring along with them, without any air of authority or display of his own opinions. Even when he was only here for a few days as in July 1951 *en route* for South Africa or on 6th to 10th August 1954 on his last voyage from France to America he made the most of his time renewing old friend-ships and beginning new ones.

Teilhard's acquaintance with British life and British scien-tists is illustrated by his familiarity with English as spoken and written. His many contributions to the Bulletin of the Geo-logical Society of China begin with the *Geology of the Weich'ang Area* (1932) and the important *Notes on Continental Geology* (1936) and culminate in the volume on *Early Man in China* [1] (1941) which replaced Dr. Davidson Black's study of Sinan-thropus (1933) and discussed with illustrations and maps the discoveries of human remains against " the general sedimentary climatic and faunistic evolution of the late Cenozoic China ". All these were written in English, and though they give occa-sional signs that this was not the author's native tongue the result is brilliantly clear and eminently readable. The fact is that he spoke English freely and happily if with a strong French accent [2] and had affectionate contacts with many natives of Britain, but had not read many English writers with academic interest or literary appreciation except those listed by Dr. Cuénot for the years of his exile during the war. Dr. Barbour testifies to the fact that he knew hardly any of the authors whom he would seem to have read—that for example

[1] Printed in Peking for the Institut de Géo-Biologie.
[2] Cuénot says that his talk with Barbour was " in an amazing jargon that would have eclipsed an Esperantist ", p. 198.

he had never heard of Henry Drummond's *Ascent of Man*,[1] and had never met the contemporary thinkers and scientists whom he so much resembles. Even in his last years, apart from his friendship with Dr. Needham, Sir Julian Huxley and Dr. J. B. S. Haldane, with several of the palaeontologists and zoologists at the British Museum and with the English Jesuits, this remains true. His thought and speech were in the language of Édouard Le Roy and Maurice Blondel not of Lloyd Morgan and Whitehead. This is no reflection upon his philosophy or wisdom—his French friends were not less learned nor lucid than their British contemporaries. But it explains why some of his critics accuse him of using unscientific language or of Gallic eloquence. And it added to his loneliness and sense of isolation.

A NOTE ON PATRIOTIC FRAUDS

If the stress here laid upon patriotic fiction seems misplaced or exaggerated, it is well to remember the similar outbreak among men of learning and, otherwise, of integrity in the middle of the sixteenth century, and to notice its effect upon one of the greatest doctors and scientists of the time, John Caius. Born at Norwich, educated at Gonville Hall, Cambridge, working for four years at Padua with Vesalius, a profound student of Galen but also author of the first clinical study of the Sweating Sickness, the friend of Conrad Gesner, for eight years President of the Royal College of Physicians, Master and Second Founder of his College in Cambridge, he published in 1568 in London an anonymous volume on the Antiquity of the University of Cambridge ; this was followed in 1574 by a second volume in which his authorship was acknowledged.[2]

[1] Older readers will remember the outstanding importance in Britain of Drummond's two books.

[2] Reprinted in *Works of John Caius*, ed. by E. S. Roberts, 1912, pp. 1–227. A brief account of the occasion of the controversy is in the *Memoir* by J. Venn, p. 52.

The books set out to challenge the claim of Oxford to be the older of the two English Universities. This seems to have alleged that when Brutus the Trojan had led his followers to Albion, occupied it and changed its name to Britannia, a party of Greeks, philosophers, came to " Greke lade " (Cricklade) near to Oxon, so named by the Saxons. Most scholars, however, were content to ascribe the foundation of Oxford to King Alured.

Caius represents the Cambridge Orator as replying that the foundation of his University at Grantecestria took place in the reign of Gurguntius in the year 375 B.C. when Cantaber was expelled from Spain, came to Britain and founded Cantabrigia. The authority for this is said to be the " Black Codex " (pp. 14 and 38). Others claim that Leland denied this and made Sigebert the founder. In any case these are pre-Christian. The University is said to have acknowledged Cantaber in a letter to King Philip of Spain dated August 1554.

Caius, however, introduced a much older date. Gildas and Polydore Vergil, he says, state that directly after Noah's flood Britain had giants as its inhabitants ; and these were men of probity and wisdom, love of letters and love of God. Berosus speaks of the best of them as Samothes ; he ruled Britons and Celts, and was succeeded by Sarro and Druys. Hence sprang the Druids mentioned by Seneca and Pliny in the sixteenth book of his Natural History—they survived from 1013 B.C. to A.D. 179 (p. 23). The giants were " earth-born " not necessarily of huge stature like Goliath or Polyphemus or Gogmagog.

Caius gives an account of the debate between Throgmorton of Oxford and John Redman and Nicholas Ridley of Cambridge, but makes this lead up to a series of royal and papal charters supposedly given to the University. These are printed in full. The first is from Arthurus dated 7th April 531 in the city of London (pp. 68–70) giving status and exemption from taxes to the teachers and students of Cambridge University. The second is from Pope Honorius dated 624 and in it is the statement that there was a University at Cambridge in the time of Pope Eleutherius (A.D. 184) before its destruction by the Danes (pp. 75, 78) : the third is from Pope Sergius dated 3rd May 689 ; and the fourth from King Cadwallader who says that the University was founded by Cantaber and honoured by many kings,[1] Lucius, Asclepiodorus Constantine, Uther Pendragon and Arthur, the date being Cambridge, 685 (pp. 92–4).

The importance of these charters and their wide acceptance in the sixteenth century is testified by their appearance in the great illuminated manuscript of such charters presented by Robert Hare in 1587 to the University and still preserved in its archives. So far as I know no one has yet discovered the origin, date and authorship of these certainly spurious documents.

[1] Of whom Sir Thomas Malory writes in *Le Morte d'Arthur*, bk. v.

CHAPTER FOUR

TEILHARD AND THE WORLD
OF MANKIND

NOT THE LEAST REMARKABLE FACT about Teilhard is that
with his profound and scientific knowledge of man's origin
and age-old evolution and with his equally profound and
religious insight into his nature, needs and possibilities, he
should have combined and in his later years developed so full
and realistic an appreciation not only of his goal but of the
present and practical steps towards it. Those who consider
and are impressed by the range of his vision into the past, and
are surprised by his power to relate it to his prediction of
Omega, the fulfilment and consummation of man's cosmos,
will hardly expect to find so realistic a series of papers as those
in which he sets out his policy for us his contemporaries at this
critical turning-point in our history. This man—as the great
scholar and preacher T. R. Glover used to say—" speaks
things ". When he turns from his almost apocalyptic dream
of the cosmogenesis and Christification of the world he translates it into the common sense of an educational and psychologically appropriate programme : for him the two are one.

It is hardly necessary to note how unusual this is among
Christian prophets or even reformers. Religion is full of prediction clothed in celestial and diabolical imagery and fore-
telling cataclysms and damnation up to the limits of human
sadism or an eternity of bliss almost equally unattractive ; full
of elaborately detailed prognostications of a Satanic Arma-
geddon or a Second Coming of Christ—events upon which

human effort has no effect and by which human freedom is sterilised. At times and for many of us the accompaniment of so-called Biblical theology has been to reduce Christian obligation to the duty of waiting passively in a world for which we can do nothing until history is brought to its sudden God-determined end.

That such a version of Christian hope and of first-century Apocalyptic should be contagious in times of strain and calamity is not inexplicable : it happens and has happened under many forms and in many religions. But that Christians of to-day should seriously and authoritatively proclaim it, is a curious comment on what we have called the great blight. Yet here is the crucial theological utterance in the Report presented to the British Council of Churches in 1959, *Christians and Atomic War* : " It is part of the secularisation of the times that men think there must be a simple way forward to broader sunlit uplands of historical progress. The Christian, while full of longing and hope, knows that history is not like that. His abiding confidence does not lie in any certainty that history will work itself out to a millennium, but rather that it will remain a struggle of good and evil till the day God chooses to complete His purpose and bring all things to their end." [1] The first of these sentences seems to contradict both the earliest proclamation of his message by Jesus,[2] and the opening petitions of the Lord's Prayer " on earth as it is in heaven ". The second is a claim to a knowledge of the significance of history which to some of us seems arrogant if not blasphemous. The third goes near to making our struggle meaningless, implies that God's purpose has no relation to our adventure, and imputes to him an arbitrary detachment irreconcilable with his Incarnation : this is a relapse from belief in his redemptive love in favour of some other and inscrutable attitude to his children. It is only fair to say that the group which drew up the Report did not contain any member highly qualified in theology. But they could hardly have written such sentences

[1] L.c. p. 22.   [2] Mark i. 15.

if they had read the brilliant page or two in the *Phenomenon* (pp. 232–3) in which Teilhard disposes unanswerably of such heresies.

It is perhaps Teilhard's greatest service to our time that having accepted the whole cosmic process as one, continuous, complexified and convergent, he can regard it with an unfaltering hope. Anyone who enters into the significance of evolution will find in the record of it evidence of progress and therefore of encouragement, not as an exception, but in its diverse forms and at every level verifiable and conclusive. His experience of the movement of it not as something external but as the whole environment in which he is wholly involved gives him a confident awareness of its reality which no knowledge of its obvious evil and pain can overthrow or in the last issue impair. Indeed, though their presence and power in God's world will always give pause to his assurance and save him from a glib or insensitive optimism, he will come to see that tragic and terrible as they are they yet have their own place in the world and are perhaps essential to its fulfilment. For Teilhard as for others of his generation this conviction of the worth of the world was reinforced by his long and heroic service in war. His particular duty as a stretcher-bearer in a front-line unit stationed for long periods on the worst sectors of the French battlefield, gave him a unique training in the ordeals of modern war—the long-continued exposure to overwhelming tension for which our normal manhood is nowadays ill-equipped and unprepared. His native toughness as an Auvergnat, devoted to constant exposure under fire for the rescue of the wounded, could not have survived if he had not discovered the thrill of action for others, the comradeship created by danger, and the reverence for the suffering and the valour of mankind. He had experienced to the full that "cleansing of the emotions by pity and fear" which Aristotle declared to be the function of tragedy ; and the man who has no sense of tragedy has little to give to God or his fellows.

The resultant certainty of the Christification of the world, that is of the universally effective operation of the redemptive power of the love that neither exploits nor sentimentalises, was expressed by Teilhard with an increasing simplicity and insistence. He had defined the cosmic movement as twofold, tangential towards wider and richer community and radial towards the divine ; [1] and this he set out in a simple diagram and in the words upward and onward " *vers l'en haut par l'en avant* ".[2] It is this conviction of the fundamental nature of the process of evolution which gives its unity, physical and spiritual, to Teilhard's philosophy. He had described it in his first exposition of the stuff of the world so as to account for the negative and positive reaction at the primal level and for the complexity and convergence of the developments to come. As an interpretation of the unity in plurality of the cosmos it is the sort of hypothesis that goes as near as any other to fit the facts. The early Greeks, our first masters in philosophy, started from the problem of the one and the many : the modern version of it, the relationship of individual and community, remains the primary issue for our own day. For Teilhard such a starting-point leads on to an eminently coherent and practicable programme for our future ; and has the great advantage which his wholehearted acceptance of evolution involves, that he is thinking not in terms of static entities in combination but of movement and action in community.

As his thought developed Teilhard realised more fully that the two aspects of the process were in fact one and inseparable. He had, as we have seen, worked out his philosophy in terms of a *weltanschauung* in which Christian and scientific elements were welded together from the start. His experience of an incarnational and sacramental theology controlled his whole concept of nature and history ; it was in the pursuit of his secular activities and the service and friendship of his neighbours that he realised the presence of Christ as not only the

[1] Cf., e.g., *Phenomenon*, pp. 64–6.
[2] Cf. " Le Cœur du problème " in *L'Avenir*, pp. 346–9.

embodiment of the divine-human unity, but the source and goal of evolution, the inspiration of man's adventure and the instrument of his individual and social integration. In the fellowship of the cosmos men and nations could win their fulfilment. The way up and on involved, as he came to see, God as all in all. The idea of a solitary and detached perfection was to him almost a contradiction in terms. For the full-grown, the Godward and the manward movement became not merely convergent but identical.

We shall later consider his *christique* more fully—how he distinguished Eastern from Western mysticism, non-attachment from agapé. But the practical steps to be taken are described under his heading of *unanimisation*, the attainment of a real unanimity as the nature and goal of human agreement, and the emergence of human solidarity. He invented his last new word *amorisation* to denote what St. Paul has called " the building up of the body in love ".[1]

The first step is the recognition early in his career and later shared with his scientific friends and especially Sir Julian Huxley, that the growing point of evolution for man and his world is no longer to be found at the level of the biological whether by natural selection or by physical mutation. With the coming of what Teilhard calls the noosphere, man's self-consciousness, intellectual cognition, communication and control, begins to dominate and supersede physical development ; nurture tends to replace nature ; the result is a vast extension of life's capacities and the opening up of unpredictable possi-bilities. If we admit the criticism that Teilhard may well have underrated the importance of genetics and of sudden muta-tions in evolution,[2] few will dispute the value of his testimony to the new epoch signalised by the emergence of man and the effects of his analytical and inventive genius. Of the character and scope of human achievement he has given a searching account in *Le Milieu divin* which surveys our outward and inward response to our divine environment, and has expanded

---

[1] Eph. iv. 16.   [2] Cf. above, pp. 61-2.

it by his later papers upon the practical problems that confront a democratic society in this nuclear age. It is notable that in so doing he pays regard both to the presence of technical discoveries and to the need for deeper psychological insights and advances. *Socialisation* he recognises as a primary factor and inescapable necessity : we must realise our oneness and establish a world-wide family-relationship by increasing in every way our mutual understanding and co-operation.

But while insisting on the importance for evolution of the human mind and its intellectual achievements, he never falls into the error of exaggerating it and so regarding man as a superior type of calculating machine. " I have tried to show ", he writes, " that we can hope for no progress without the primacy and triumph of the personal at the summit of mind." [1] This is his conviction from the first and explains his insistence upon agapé as the supreme and divine quality. His own modesty, friendliness and sociability (and he combined the three to a remarkable degree) are characteristic of him from his youth : and his wide interests and world-wide travels gave him rich opportunity for their exercise. The result is that in his later years when publicity and freedom of movement were denied to him, he set himself to emphasise what he had at first along with his friend Le Roy called *hominisation*.

For the growth of this concern for human relationships and for the study of national and racial partnership his own temperament and experience were increasingly important. He developed a genius for friendship. In his pastoral dealings with individuals both men and women, in the team-work of his seminars and laboratory, in the intimate contacts of travel, of exploration and of physical hardships, and in the carefully planned conferences and public discussions, his gaiety and wit, his insight and sensibility, his speed of mind and his mastery of speech made him at once a good colleague and an outstanding contributor. Those who met him even casually on a ship or permanently for weeks of digging carried away vivid

[1] *Phenomenon*, p. 297.

and affectionate memories. With his colleagues, for example with the group of a dozen scientists gathered in Peking in 1927,[1] his relationship was deep and intimate, undiminished by exile from the country dearest to his heart : in West or East, indeed everywhere in his much-travelled life, he remained singularly consistent, sensitive and responsive. There can be few men even to-day who have known at close quarters a larger number of human varieties ; and perhaps no one about whom their testimony is more closely similar or more deeply appreciative. The " reéseau Teilhard ", as Cuénot calls it, was a very real international community. " He is one of us " as Teilhard used to say.

It is unnecessary in view of Dr. Cuénot's detailed list of his travels and of his own *Letters from a Traveller* to give any full account of the years of almost perpetual movement [2] which began with his first visit when he joined Émile Licent at Tientsin in 1923 and continued until his death. During the years before the Second World War he visited China continually and indeed was kept there under Japanese control from 1939 till 1945.

Cuénot in the third section of his book, especially pp. 63–77 and 90–109, has given a full account of his two exploratory tours—the second, April 1926 to August 1927—after his virtual exile from Paris, spent mostly in Peking, and of the many friends and colleagues whom he met, J. Gunnar Andersson the Swede who with V. K. Ting, the first Director and Wong Wen-Hao, whom Teilhard had met in Belgium, his assistant and successor, had established the Geological Survey of China ; Sven Hedin the explorer then on his way to Turkestan ; [3] A. W. Grabau the American and Davidson Black from Canada of the Peking Medical College, of whom Teilhard wrote with deep affection ; H. F. Osborn the creator of the American

[1] Cf. *Letters from a Traveller*, p. 138.
[2] An excellent summary of these is given by Dr. Tindell Hopwood in *Proceedings of Linnean Soc.*, vol. 67, p. 141.
[3] Cf. his letter of 22nd May 1941 to Teilhard (Cuénot, p. 188).

Museum and the " grand seigneur " of American biology and palaeontology who published the first account of Teilhard in 1931 ; [1] and above all George B. Barbour of Edinburgh and Cambridge Universities, the Scottish geologist who had been surveying Kalgan north of Peking since 1922, took Teilhard to the valley of Sang Kan-ho in 1923, was his constant companion in China until he left for a professorship in Cincinnati in 1932, and was always one of his closest friends, sharing his scientific and religious interests and joining in many of his adventures in the field and in America. From the first their partnership was complete : in 1958 Barbour wrote to Dr. Cuénot : " All that I had was his ; the discoveries that I made were shared with him : they were his as much as mine. Add to this a personal affection and intimacy that left no room for explanations or apologies. Teilhard treated me as a younger brother. The work of one of us supplemented that of the other as our knowledge of the geology of China increased. Of all the men with whom I have lived he was the most noble." [2]

In later residences in China Teilhard spent nine months, May 1931 to February 1932, on the journey of the Yellow Cruise from Peking to Kashgar in west Turkestan and back, alone among the engineers and mechanics of the Citroën party, an adventure described in several books [3] and mentioned in his own letters, [4] under the leadership of G. M. Haardt whose death just before the journey's end gave him deep sorrow. [5] Teilhard though unable to do much continuous work was free to observe and record the characteristics of regions almost wholly unknown, and in April 1936 presented through M. P.

[1] In *American Museum Novitates*, no. 485, pp. 1-13.
[2] Cuénot, p. 191.
[3] For a list of Cuénot, p. 159.
[4] *Letters from a Traveller*, pp. 174-92.
[5] Cf. the long letter to his widow about their son Claude in Cuénot, pp. 136-8.

Jodot a report on the geology of the Turfan area south of Tienshan previously visited by his friend Sven Hedin.[1]

After central Asia in the Yellow Cruise, Teilhard set himself to explore with Barbour middle and southern China. They toured Shansi by cart in 1933.[2] Up the Yangtze to Szechwan almost into Tibet in the spring of 1934 ; to Honan in the autumn ; and in 1935 to Kwangsi and Yunnan this time by boat from Shanghai to Canton and thence south and west nearly to Tonkin. Black's death in 1934 and the increasing strain of the Japanese war produced a new group of scientists in Peking. There were several younger Chinese, Pei Wen-Chung a bright and charming man who was sent to Paris in 1936 to study with Breuil, and is now Director of the Institute of Prehistory, who still retains happy memories of Teilhard ; his compatriot Yang Chung-Chien who had also worked in Europe, and Chia Lan-Po, both closely connected with the exploration of Chou-Kou-Tien to which Teilhard devoted himself from 1933 onwards and on which the three collaborated with him in various reports. Franz Weidenreich, Black's successor, who reconstructed " Nelly " the female Sinanthrope modelled by Mrs. Lucile Swan ;[3] Helmut de Terra the American[4] whom Teilhard met in Washington in 1934 and again in September 1934 when he went to Bombay and with him and T. T. Paterson to Kashmir and the Siwalik Hills south of Simla, the Valley of the Indus to Sukkur and so by the river Narbada, the Central Plain and Hoshangabad to Calcutta and afterwards to Burma and Java ;[5] Ralph von Koenigswald, of Danish-German parentage, appointed as

[1] Cf. *Sommaire Soc. Géol. de France* (1936), pp. 129–30.

[2] As described by Barbour *The World of Chardin*, pp. 30–1, and Cuénot, pp. 222–8.

[3] She did Teilhard's bust pictured by Cuénot and now in the Museum of Natural History in New York. Cf. *Letters from a Traveller*, p. 233, and her article in *The Wind and The Rain*, pp. 40–9 (London, 1962).

[4] His regard for Teilhard is expressed in words almost identical with those of Barbour, cf. Cuénot, p. 195.

[5] Cf. *Letters from a Traveller*, pp. 210–21.

palaeontologist to the geological service in Java and working there from 1930 to 1946, who entertained Teilhard on his two visits in 1935 and 1938 to the island to see his discoveries of Pithecanthropus ; and H. L. Movius of Harvard whom he met in Burma in 1938 ; these represent the principal colleagues of his years of perpetual movement, and his affection for them in all their variety of background and race is proof that if he was an optimist concerning human nature, he at least knew what he was talking about. For his contacts were not of the sheltered or academic sort : his friends met him not only in the pulpit but in the rough and under sufficiently trying cir-cumstances. Here is a typical description of the last stages of his voyage back to China in 1937, " It was passed very well in spite of cholera in Hong Kong, the blockade along the coasts and a typhoon at Kobe." [1]

In addition to his Asiatic journeys he spent a year in France in 1927–28 renewing contact with his friends and family, and ending up with a visit to French Somaliland with Henri de Monfreid and his wife whom he met on the voyage out in April 1926. Monfreid's first account of " this great devil of a priest, so lean and strong, such a contrast to the usual unctuous cleric " led him to nickname him " the pirate " : later he wrote, " he was my brother from that moment : an extra-ordinary man ; nothing turbid about him. Nothing shady. Clear as crystal, and diffusing a divine radiance. The man was radiant ; one cannot measure such." [2] The expedition from Obock to Harar and Diredawa in Abyssinia and back to Djibouti was a delight to Teilhard, to Pierre Lamare the geologist of Bordeaux and his old friend, and to their hosts—his stories of the miracle of the tiny train and of the cave full of wasps [3] have the true epic flavour.

Five times at least he visited America. The first was in February 1931 for a conference in New York where he met

[1] Letter of 15th October, Cuénot, p. 185.
[2] Cf. Cuénot, pp. 87 and 114–25, for the expedition.
[3] Cuénot, pp. 119 and 121.

Osborn, Nelson and R. C. Andrews, already his friends, a meeting in Columbia University to discuss the Yellow Cruise expedition with its leader G. M. Haardt and a visit to Paul Claudel the poet.[1] He went on to Chicago to see the Field Museum and so to San Francisco. He returned to China by way of Honolulu where he was shown Hawaii by the geologist W. K. Gregory, and Japan, landing at Kobe and visiting Kyoto, and having written his *L'Esprit de la terre* on the voyage. On this first tour of the United States he noted that most American scientists, though well-qualified and able, identified evolution with a materialistic outlook.[2] His second visit was in the summer of 1933 for a Conference of Geology in Washington where he met Barbour now settled in Cincinnati, crossed the continent with him and others by Pullman,[3] and planned further expeditions with him : and then in April 1937 when he crossed by way of Tokio and Seattle to Philadelphia for a small symposium of experts convened by the Carnegie Foundation through de Terra and including von Koenigswald and Dr. Garrod. On this occasion his purpose was to form a committee for planned and endowed research into the prehistory of China, India and Malaya with the help of H. D. Collings of the Raffles Museum in Singapore and Teilhard's Chinese colleagues. The scheme was fulfilled in the following year, when de Terra, Movius and Teilhard spent three months in Burma, and then joined von Koenigswald in Java during March and April. Thence he sailed from Singapore and was back in China till September 1938 when he left again for Japan to see Père Leroy, and for a fourth visit to Vancouver, Harvard and New York, and so to France. Then after a brief stay in England he returned in March 1939 to America for a Geological conference at Berkeley in June, and reached Peking on 30th August.

[1] Cf. *Letters from a Traveller*, pp. 167–73.
[2] Cuénot, pp. 143, 188.
[3] Cf. Cuénot, p. 199 ; Barbour in *The World of Teilhard*, p. 29. Sir Arthur and Lady Smith Woodward accompanied this " C2 excursion ".

The twelve years that separated his expulsion from the Institut in 1926 with its consequent ban upon his holding any post that might be offered to him in Paris, and the permission to him in 1938 to accept the laboratory under the Institute of Human Palæontology offered to him by the Minister Jean Zay, were not only an exile but the beginning of a new life. His work during that period was continuous and very hard, involving perpetual journeying and the experience of a satisfying internationalism. He had made the sacrifice of his home and career when he accepted the discipline imposed by his Society and Church. He had offered himself and his world in *La Messe sur le monde* and confessed his surrender of it in *Le Milieu divin.* On that issue his inner conflict was over, " It seems to me that I have never been at once more impassioned and secure in my faith in the Universe and more profoundly indifferent to what affects me personally or what is in the small sense human in the world ".[1] Already in 1927 he was beginning to plan the *Phenomenon of Man*, and in 1931 had produced the first version of it in *L'Esprit de la terre*, and while he was growing into a fuller consciousness of the scale and universality of his message he was exploring it along three lines of intense mental, physical and social activity.

First his pan-Christic mysticism, as Cuénot calls it, deepened as his sense of human and cosmic unity was enlarged by the practical business of travel and friendship ; and his concept of the noosphere as the new phase of evolution expanded with it. Here was the double and yet concurrent movement " upward and onward " whose rudiments he found in the earliest energy of the universe and which was converging towards the Omega-point of fulfilment. His mind and soul were kept at stretch even when his body was worked to exhaustion by travel and digging.

For during this very period he had taken over the completion of Black's great discovery of primitive man in the

[1] Letter of 31st July 1930—Cuénot, p. 150.

limestone cliff of Chou-Kou-Tien by the thorough exploration
of its series of six fissures for evidence both of the contemporary
mammale and of the physical and cultural characteristics of
Sinanthropus. Pei and Yang his colleagues testify to his persistence in sticking to the complete programme in spite of the
upheavals in China and the invasion by Japan ; and the resulting reports were largely of his composition. That the
work expanded to expeditions into other huge areas of China
and so into India, Burma and Java before the end of the period
is proof of the extent to which Teilhard's mastery of the
subject and tireless energy contributed to the whole world-
wide effort to solve the problems of human evolution and
social development.

In addition there was the special task of relating the new
knowledge of man's character and capacity to the traditional
religions of the world and specifically to the Catholic Church.
Teilhard's own temperament in spite of what is so freely called
his mysticism was active, creative and social. Even in his
devotions there is more of passion than of quietism, of identification with God in the world than of non-attachment or
escapism. He shows little sign of sympathy with the *Via
negativa* or its Catholic advocates ; and when he went to the
East it was with no predisposition to the religion of the begging-
bowl and the hermitage.[1] At first his condemnation of Eastern
religions as out of date and particularly for their treatment of
women was severe, yet even in 1923 he could add "they
showed such exuberant possibilities in philosophy and mysticism and human morals that one can never think of humanity
as definitely confined within a strait waistcoat of precepts"
and in 1932 "I see the necessity of freeing our religion from
all that is specifically mediterranean."

The integration of his religious and scientific work in an
increasing universalism of outlook was stimulated by the international crisis which confronted him on his later visits to
Europe and America. Like most of the survivors of the First

[1] Cf. *La Route de l'ouest*, 1932.

85

World War he found it scarcely possible to believe that a second holocaust could come within twenty years; and his faith in humanity strengthened by his happy experiences of scientific co-operation made it harder for him than for others. But no one in Western Europe in 1937 and 1938 could doubt the gravity of the Nazi threat to peace or evade the responsibility of thinking out his own position towards it. Teilhard was constrained to apply the convictions drawn from his whole experience to the practical issues and anxieties of the time. He must condense his philosophy into a policy and apply it to the concrete situation. As we have seen, he had the necessary equipment, the courage based upon a full acquaintance with war and an indifference to his individual destiny, the wisdom due to his habit of thinking in terms of epochs of time and a field as wide as the world, and the religion which he had come to apply to his whole outlook and way of life. He had begun to plan and execute his great work on the story of man's evolution, which was to take its final shape in the *Phenomenon of Man*. It was hardly an intrusion upon his task to set out an appeal to his fellow-countrymen and all whom he could reach that they should realise the greatness of their present possibilities, rise above the individual and national rivalries that threatened world-wide ruin, and devote themselves to the service not of a nation or an ideology but of humanity. The document deserves attention in some detail.

In 1939 when he came back—as it turned out—for the last time to China a tired and very troubled man, he had already written and circulated to his friends his " Reflections on the present Crisis "[1] the appeal called *Sauvons l'humanité*. He had lived until then in the hope that our troubles were just the final manifestations of a hurricane of the past " and that life would eventually go on as before ". Now had come the

---

[1] With this title it was cyclostyled from Peking on 11th November 1936. It was printed in France with a preface by his friend M. H. Bégouen in February 1940. For his first account of it cf. *Letters from a Traveller*, p. 228. It has now been printed in Cahier 3, pp. 67-97.

proof that mankind was entering a period of unprecedented change. " Anxiety about it had shaken even the calm of our laboratories " and " we geologists and prehistorians whose business it is to deal with vast epochs of duration must try to read the signs of the times." So he prefaces the essay in which he outlines his convictions as to our faith and opportunity.

The contents of his message fall into four headings—a faith in the future of mankind, a knowledge of human progress, a policy for a human " front ", and finally a recognition of the place of Christianity.

He begins with a sensitive examination of the several causes of our present pessimism. Defeatism is the basic weakness of the time : can we prove it false, not sentimentally but object-ively and rationally ? He points first to the progress of the past century, the world-wide spread of civilisation and of shared knowledge. Only universal destruction could bring on us the fate of Egypt or Athens. More convincing is our new knowledge of the past, present and future of mankind, his unique status and cosmic significance. The record of our evolution proves that through all its failures and problems and in spite of Spengler, we advance. Three characteristics of our progress can be defined : it is *limitless*—the future sets no bounds to its irreversible spirituality ; it is *total* involving the whole range of human effort from politics and economics to science and religion ; it is *personal* so that in it the individual finds his fulfilment in the collective.

He then faces the practical tensions of the crisis, the conflict between three dominant ideologies, democracy, communism and fascism ; and these correspond to the three characteristics already described. Democracy, the eldest child of the French Revolution, has a boundless faith in the future, but it has mis-taken equality for liberty and the crowd for the community. Communism has a vision of the material unity of mankind, but in reaction against the anarchic liberalism of democracy has suppressed personality and reduced community to the level of the termite, so endangering its own ideal of Universalism.

87

Fascism in fact repudiates the Revolution and the Modern World in favour of a return to a doctrine of the chosen people, a conservatism almost neolithic, a future which rejects the concepts of the universal and the unlimited in favour of the partial and the privileged. It is easy to denounce these three as proofs of decadence and the failure of civilisation ; yet each, however defective in itself, is rather constructive than destructive ; and each could contribute something of value if unified with the others.

So he issues his demand for a " Front humain " to take the place of a " front fasciste " or a " front populaire ", for a fourth spirit to combine the democratic valuation of the person with the communist vision of material efficiency and the fascist ideal of organised élites. At present the mass of mankind lives unsatisfied : neither left nor right is progressive in the true sense. We join one or other but find them at bottom anxious and frustrated. We want something larger, more comprehensive, more beautiful. Our fathers worked for the rights of man ; they could have no knowledge of the scale or dimensions or harmony of the world such as we possess who have all time and all space in which to serve the rights of the World, the Future, the Universal and the Personal. We have all the resources necessary for such service ; and we could in fact secure their full use if we could realise that there are at bottom only two groups dividing mankind, those who believe in future progress and will risk everything for it and those who through listlessness, selfishness or discouragement do not want to advance and are afraid to do so. Fear, though the most familiar incentive to unity, is a poor substitute for the love of life which has brought us to our present mastery of nature. This cannot be inspired by mere abstractions ; and concrete projects too easily distract, dissipate and pervert our ventures into trivial and useless ends. We must find our El Dorado—our tangible, practicable and satisfying goal ; and for this end must enlist engineers and technicians capable of exploring and satisfying our true aspirations. Perhaps the great challenge presented to us by science is no other than the discovery of God.

Finally he confesses that in view of this, even if he were not a Christian, he would in such an analysis find room for Christendom not only because of its general influence on modern civilisation but because in the present struggle it is intimately concerned. For as we have seen, this struggle obviously involves conflicting concepts of life and of the world. Moreover Humanism tends to become a new religion—and is plain evidence of a basically religious outlook in mankind. How ought Christendom to react to it ?

The relationship of Humanist and Christian will remain obscure until we treat them on the issues that they have in common. " We can resolve the difficulties if we realise that the guiding principles of Christ's religion are exactly those which express the essence of the human effort : Heaven, Catholicity, Community of Souls—these are the Future, the Universal, the Personal. On these terms comparison becomes possible." He examines in detail the concept of future progress which science has recently so vastly enlarged. In the hundreds of millions of years that astronomers allot to the Earth we must look for vast developments not only in our physical but in our psychological and spiritual capacity and for space and time to enable unpredictable growth : " new heavens and a new earth " is not mere poetry. Then he turns to personality. Science too often dwells only on cosmic immensities and the collective power of social organisation—a diffused energy and a " state without heart or face ", an unattractive deity. Christianity must intervene to restore human aspirations on lines appropriate to the structural laws of man's being and life. No doubt nothing could appear more out of date and anthropomorphic than the personal God of the Christian. Yet alongside of him the Gospel discloses the most modern of religions. Instead of a humanity in danger of being swallowed up by philosophic determinisms and social machineries Christianity maintains the primacy of reflective, that is of personalised thought, the possibility of a central and universal conscience and of the development of a direct awareness of this centre upon which everything converges. The figure of the Christ as realised concretely in Christian experience is the most perfect representation of a final and complete objective that the universal effort of mankind can attain. Why is this so often despised ?

The supposed conflict between Faith and Progress has done more harm to Christendom than the fiercest persecutions. It arises out of our failure to adjust ourselves to the three components of our spirit. Christianity is universalist ; but it is still tied up with mediaeval cosmology and has never enlarged its view of the Incarnation to fit the immensities of to-day. It is futurist ; but it has let its ideas of transcendence become other-worldly, not super-worldly. It is supremely personalist ; but is dominated by insistence upon legalism and morality instead of manifesting the organic and cosmic splendours of the universal Christ. " Christianity will only be reborn when it re-incarnates itself and aligns itself freely and resolutely with what we have called the Human Front."

So in a short and brilliantly articulated essay he outlines the results of his experiences and the headlines of his subsequent work. From it he turned to the completion of the *Phénomène humain*, of which a complete version was made during his exile in China from 1939 to 1941[1] and sent to Rome for approval. It was then rejected, and he thoroughly revised the final script which he took with him to the Holy City in 1948 but was given no opportunity of discussing. The length of time devoted to it at varying stages of his later life and his desire not only to appeal to his fellow-scientists but to forestall or avert criticism from the papal authorities make it in places difficult to follow and sometimes to interpret. As compared with the appeal it deals in much greater fullness with the

[1] In a letter of 8th February 1940 to Max Bégouen he says that he wrote one or two pages daily, *Letters from a Traveller*, p. 257; for its completion, cf. p. 284.

details of the evolutionary process ; it is an exposition rather than a piece of apologetic ; and it lays a greater stress upon love than upon " action " and stresses " unanimisation " rather than universality. But it is plainly his considered plan for giving the sense of continuity and completeness to the " futurism " which he had regarded as the primary constituent of his programme for mankind.

During the war years the courage and confidence which had inspired this message were severely strained. Peking was under the Japanese : life there was restricted and lonely. The small French colony was gradually deprived of its numerous American neighbours : no newcomers arrived : the Western world, especially after the fall of France, and the Pacific after Pearl Harbour were cut off : news of individuals was scarce and irregular : accommodation was bad : prospects grew worse. Teilhard's cheerfulness and confidence, his friendly visits and Sunday picnics, his meetings and lectures were the life of the little community. " In that time ", wrote his friend Mme Dorget in 1941,[1] " I owed to him my only moments of spiritual and moral exaltation. He kept hope and faith in true values alive in me. His attitude could astonish : but his friends realised without a shadow of doubt that he was never insensitive to the evils of mankind. His was the outlook of a man whose spirit already freed had reached the summit of the great evolutionary process in which he regarded us all as inextricably involved. The weakness of men ! Yes, surely. But their grandeur, their spark of divinity which he always knew how to discover ! What faith he had ! What goodness ! "

His confidence in human progress had of course to face the criticism of certain geneticists who argued that no demonstrable change had taken place in man's physical endowment since the days of Cro-magnon, that acquired characteristics could not be demonstrably transmitted, and that therefore human advance remained a feeble and precarious attainment.

[1] *Letters from a Traveller*, pp. 279–80. The Dorgets left for Japan in 1943.

Teilhard was, as we have admitted, slow to recognise the facts of inheritance, and the importance of mutations in the story of evolution. But on this matter he speaks precisely, taking as his point of attack Jean Rostand the great expert on anthropology and quoting his book *Pensées d'un biologiste*, pp. 32-5, in his own paper *La Formation de la noosphère*.[1] He insists that even if the long period since the emergence of Man has seen no chromosome changes (a matter on which not even Rostand can have full knowledge) yet other alterations of a radical kind have taken place. We are now living in new dimensions social, spacial and temporal which involve not only the alteration of our whole environment but an immense extension of our range of sensitiveness, exploration and control. Man may be physically similar to his remote ancestry, to Sinanthropus whom Teilhard particularly studied, but in all other respects he has achieved unpredictable marvels of development and multiplied his own understanding and influence by capabilities ranging from the electron microscope to molecular analysis, from radar to television, and from virus control to nuclear fission. Teilhard would seem to have realised and possibly heard how the work of J. M. Baldwin in America [2] and of Lloyd Morgan in Britain had demonstrated the intimacy of the relationship between organism and environment and how this proved that the controversy between Darwinism and Lamarck was an over-simplification of the issues.

Teilhard's sense of the wholeness of the cosmos and the total " immersion " of every part in it gave him not only a conviction of the solidarity and unity of the world but of the scope and method of man's co-operation with it. This led him to a growing concern with the disclosures of experimental psychology and the work of C. G. Jung and Professor Rhine. Alongside of the inventions which extended man's knowledge

[1] Printed in *L'Avenir*, p. 201, from *Rev. des Quest. Scient.*, January 1947, pp. 7-35.

[2] Cf. his *Development and Evolution* and the work of H. F. Osborn and later G. G. Simpson.

and contacts he realised that within man himself there were faculties hardly yet exercised and ranges of communication still to be explored. Anyone who is at all familiar with recent research upon the dances of bees or the migration of birds or the intelligence and playfulness of dolphins will appreciate the wisdom of Teilhard's plea for intensified and co-ordinated research, and will be confident that by it vague terms like extrasensory perception could speedily be given precise and practicable meaning. Very interesting in this connection is Dr. M. Pobers' account of a talk with him about the phenomena which Pobers, an expert Dutch parapsychologist, had been studying in the obeah and voodoo ceremonies in Jamaica and Haiti.[1]

If the lines of convergence opened up by the recent discoveries that have eliminated the barriers of geological space and solar time, and are challenging the specifically human segregations of race and class and sex, are to be followed, Teilhard foresaw three principal tasks which the new human community must undertake and which would fulfil the threefold requirement of his Human Front. These he set out simply as " the organisation of research, the concentration of research upon the subject of man, and the conjunction of science and religion : these are three natural terms of one and the same progression." [2]

His meaning in this threefold programme is amplified and made concrete in the eloquent passage written after the achievement of nuclear fission by the experiment in Arizona.[3] Impressed profoundly not only by the epoch-making character of the event but by the marvel that intense and coordinated research shared by thousands of men, had within three years discovered methods which in isolation would have involved an era of effort, he concluded that nothing in the universe need be insuperable if only sufficient numbers of ardent partners could be grouped and organised. So he

[1] Cf. Cuénot, p. 377.   [2] *Phenomenon*, p. 278.
[3] " Reflections ", September 1946 in *L'Avenir*, pp. 179–87.

conjectured that this first immense achievement might be only the prelude of a series of fantastic discoveries which would open up one by one the sealed secrets of present-day science. The vitalisation of matter by the building up of super-molecules ; the remodelling of the human organism by hormonic activity ; the control of heredity and sex by management of genes and chromosomes ; the refashioning and release of our true selves by the probing of their depths by psycho-analysis ; and the awakening and fixing of unexplored powers of mind and sensibility still dormant in mankind ; so he dreamed, confident that with world-wide encouragement some such programme was practicable.

One further question remains to be asked. Teilhard was a priest of the Roman Catholic Church and a member of the Society of Jesus ; and all attempts to persuade him that his views made it impossible for him to retain these offices were met by firm and reasoned refusal. He was prepared to accept the prohibitions and penalties restricting the publication and prescribing the place of his work ; and in spite of all his efforts to get the sentence altered, his failure led to no sign of rebellion. Nevertheless he did in fact continue to maintain his witness by insisting upon the importance of humanism, urging the need to widen the frontiers of Catholic dogma and practice, and interpreting the tradition (where possible) so as to bring larger spheres of life and work within its orbit. These three points deserve consideration.

The first arose from and was much stimulated by his friendship for many of his scientific colleagues. Men like Davidson Black of the Cenozoic Research Laboratory in China or G. M. Haardt of the Yellow Cruise or Lucien Cuénot the great biologist[1] had filled him with admiration for their qualities and with heart-searching by their rejection of his faith. He could not refuse to admire ; nor avoid trying to

---

[1] Cf. Cuénot, pp. 331-2. He published in 1931 his *L'État présent du transformisme* to which Teilhard was much indebted. Teilhard writing his last letter to him (17th May 1950) addressed him as " Master and Friend ".

meet their challenge. In no other issue did he experience so keenly the conflict between the new and the old, which in his own life had been so naturally settled. His later experiences had convinced him that the cleavage though deep and often estranging was not in itself fundamental, but the sincerity of his devotion to his Church as embodying the Christian religion prevented him from disguising its difficulty or dismissing his knowledge of its extent and seriousness. He was at once convinced that to leave religion out of account was impossible for a mature person, and that to dismiss the special quality and claim of Christianity was mistaken, but he was aware that the obstacles which so many of his contemporaries found in it arose not only from their ignorance of its real character but from the failure of Christians to reconcile their beliefs with the new knowledge or to reject opinions which are both out of date and actually subversive of truth.

It was with this problem weighing heavily upon him that he set to work on his return to Paris in 1944. Among the friends whom he made at that time were two English scientists and scholars actively concerned with the international plans that led up to Unesco. The first of these was Dr. Joseph Needham, the Reader in Biochemistry at Cambridge, who like himself had lately returned from his long war-time work in China. Needham, already eminent as a scientist but encyclopaedic in his interests, was deeply concerned with religion and with the social and international situation especially in relation to the East. At their first meeting he recognised in Teilhard " a man of the greatest intellectual honesty and sincerity combined with a prophetic Blake-like vision ".[1] He noted the originality and importance of his conviction as to convergent integration and the development within the noosphere of a super-personal organism culminating at the Omega point, and as to the interpretation of the whole evolutionary process in terms of a cosmogenesis. He realised that Teilhard had had little contact with English thought on the subject,

[1] Cf. *New Statesman*, 7th November 1959, and below, pp. 209.

with Whitehead or Lloyd Morgan, but saw that his work was
closely similar to theirs.

Unfortunately at the time his own commitments gave him
no opportunity to follow up lines of thought which he described as " abundantly worth pondering " : and his subsequent dedication to his monumental volumes on Chinese
Science made close study of Teilhard impossible. His review
of the *Phenomenon* in the *New Statesman* is one of the best
accounts of Teilhard, and of all Englishmen he is perhaps the
best qualified to understand him.

Teilhard's interest in Humanism must have been powerfully stimulated by his friendship with Sir Julian Huxley. This
also began in 1944 in Paris when Huxley was producing his
book *The Uniqueness of Man* ; and after some correspondence
the two men met in 1946 and speedily discovered the similarity
of their views upon the place of man in the history of evolution : their agreement was accompanied by a strong mutual
attraction deepening quickly into friendship. Teilhard, who
always liked the English, was delighted to find one who
shared his idea of the noosphere as a new level in the Earth's
development. He appreciated Huxley's social and intellectual
gifts, and revised his own rather dim opinion of Unesco when
he became its Director. In 1950 Huxley sent him his paper
on *Evolutionary Humanism*, and soon after, his *New Bottles for
New Wine*, and the interchange thus begun continued till 1955.
They agreed, as Huxley claims, to treat man and his place in
the cosmos solely as a phenomenon—that is without reference
to metaphysics, ethics or theology ; and on this their basic
agreement was cordial and manifestly sincere. The fact that
when the English translation of the *Phenomenon* was published
Huxley introduced it with such warmth is proof not only of
their mutual appreciation but of their genuine affection.[1]

Nevertheless it is strange that with one so concerned and
so deeply religious as Teilhard his friend has so little understanding of the place of Christian conviction in his thought.

[1] For this see Huxley's article in *Encounter*, April 1956.

This is indicated when he writes of Teilhard feeling it "imperative to try to reconcile" his scientific outlook with his religious beliefs.[1] It confirms the opinion that Sir Julian does not easily understand ideas which he is not prepared to accept —an opinion which ever since he wrote *Religion without Revelation* has been difficult to reject and which his recent articles in the Sunday press obviously confirm.[2]

Another interesting scientist with whom Teilhard made contact early in 1947 was Théodore Monod, son of a French Protestant pasteur, and himself Professor at the Museum and Director of the Institut Français d'Afrique Noire at Dakar in West Africa. Monod lost no time in urging the visit which was planned for that autumn with Barbour to the sites near Kimberley and Johannesburg. He was himself a naturalist with wide knowledge of botany and zoology, a deep concern for religion and for Africa, an impressive personality and a delightful sense of humour. He had just printed a second and complete edition of his miscellany *L'Hippopotame et le philosophe* (Paris, 1946) in which the paper on the maladies of prehistoric man must have fascinated Teilhard. The two men became close friends and regular correspondents until the visit postponed in 1947 had been fulfilled and repeated. They last met when Teilhard visited Paris in 1954[3] after letters had passed between them in which Teilhard had urged him to have a search made for localities in Angola geologically similar to those in the south and east.[4]

The second of these proposals of which we have already spoken seems to have been enunciated after his visit to the Jade Buddha. There, north-west of the imperial palace in Peking "in a little wood on a very little hill", stood a tiny

[1] *Phenomenon*, p. 22.

[2] It is I think clear that Dr. Cuénot (e.g. on p. 369) exaggerates Huxley's sympathy towards religion and ignores the depth of his prejudices against Christianity. Teilhard before his death was of course well aware of it.

[3] See below, p. 110.

[4] Cf. Cuénot, pp. 405–6, letters of 1953.

Buddhist temple containing a great statue in grey limestone ; a statue with a beautiful face "radiant with quiet joy, the calm of happiness, with a trace of a smile, the dawning of a smile". So Abbé Breuil describes it. And Teilhard loved it. He as we know had criticised the East, its effect on its women, its rejection of social welfare, its detachment from service and obligation. But this joy—his comments upon Christian communities and congregations do not disclose it. If Buddhism can produce this smile, then we cannot set it outside the socialisation and unity of the future. This conviction that the essential unity of the cosmos would one day be attained at the personal or super-personal level is significantly illustrated by the incident described in the Introduction to the first volume of the *Lettres de voyage*. He had met in some corner of the world a wholly unexpected friend who was amazed at the warmth of his welcome, "Why am I so happy, my dear friend," said the great traveller : "it is because the earth is round !"[1]

The third is concerned with his priesthood and was the subject of much thought and far-reaching proposals. He was a priest, set apart to witness and minister to "the sublime law of sacrifice" which Christ, the great high-priest, the fulfilment of all priesthood, had maintained by his self-offering on the Cross. Life was self-offering : only he who in one form or another lays down his life enters into life's fulfilment. It is not likely that Teilhard was acquainted with the confession of Jean Henri Fabre, the great naturalist to whom Bergson was so indebted, that all nature seemed obedient to such a law of sacrifice. But the fact remains that he saw priestliness in all self-giving and regarded it as a universal condition and fulfilment of real life. So he could claim, as he does explicitly in *Le Milieu*,[2] that everyone who contributes by thought or labour to the welfare of the community belongs to a "holy order", a priesthood with a special and sacerdotal function.

[1] *Letters from a Traveller*, p. 55, and more fully by Barbour in *The World of Teilhard*, p. 24.　　　　[2] E.g. pp. 39–43.

He actually urged that butchers or bakers or any who regarded their work primarily as a vocation for the fuller life of the world should be encouraged to band themselves together as fulfilling a divine ministry within the one divine community. Thus in spite of his insistence upon and delight in his own priesthood he had stripped it of any sense of exclusive or privileged superiority. We were all members one of another, equal in status though differing in function ; and any claim to exclusive worth was an insult to God. It is notable, though in view of his devotion to his sister and his happy relations with women hardly surprising, that he seems to have applied exactly the same concept of sacrificial ministry to them as to himself.

To express his vision so—in terms of vocation and ministry —may be to suggest an idealising and sentimental estimate of human possibilities ; and much that has been written about Teilhard stresses his charm and friendliness as if these were the predominant qualities of his character. In his personal dealings affection played a large part ; and the impression of it colours too strongly the attitude of many of his disciples. But behind it and controlling it was the shrewd and independent judgment of the Auvergnat, and the disconcerting insight and wit of his Voltairean heritage. We have already quoted his pungent comments upon British scientists. Equally forthright and illuminating is his diagnosis of the fundamental weakness of Unesco.[1] With Sir Julian Huxley he was on terms of friendship and affection : of the organisation and its intentions he was hopeful and appreciative : but of the difference between professions and achievements he was lucidly aware ; and his diagnosis though unpopular was made plainly and without apology. Unesco suffered from having found employment for an " upper house " whose qualifications were social status rather than intellectual competence, capacity for

---

[1] A similar example of insight and candour is found in his letter on the American election of 1952, cf. *Letters from a Traveller*, pp. 334–5, with its brilliant prediction of the Republican " sharks " and J. Foster Dulles.

hard work, or specialised knowledge.[1] He believed it was too comfortable to face the austerities and demands of the world ; he wanted action rather than resolutions, and did not see in it the sense of urgency and concentration that could bring its programmes to life.

His own particular gifts lay not only in his skill in discussion and readiness to investigate and debate large international issues but in his ability to bring the results down to earth and to devote himself personally to the sheer hard work of travel, investigation and remedial action. Very characteristic is his reply to Professor Watson when asked how one of his great journeys from Peking had been managed. His questioner expected the names of boats or rail-roads : Teilhard replied, " I walked."

It is this combination that makes his concern for the future so important and so stimulating. He saw the means as well as the end, and did not ignore or evade the necessity of drudgery. From his study of the millennia involved in human origins he could gauge the time-factor without being overwhelmed or disheartened by it ; and for the evolutionist action here and now was the end product of discussion and diagnosis. His life's work had made him a digger and sifter, and he did not believe that the future of mankind could be achieved in the salons or the laboratories alone.

---

[1] Cuénot, p. 362 n., quotes Teilhard's letter of 28th March 1951 : he expressly excepts Huxley from this criticism.

CHAPTER FIVE

TEILHARD AND THE
WORLD WITHIN

IT IS, AS WE HAVE SEEN, characteristic of Teilhard that along with his wide and passionate interest in his whole local and cosmic environment and his belief in " action " as Blondel defined it, he should be and show himself to be one of the greatest modern revealers of the inner life of contemplation and adoration. Those English readers who first met him in the objective and difficult pages of the *Phenomenon* must surely have felt almost startled when they found themselves in the world of insight and intimacy of the *Milieu*. Books of devotion have in any case, and for most of us, a strange and usually exotic flavour—their language is archaic, often sentimental and affected ; we feel that it is peculiar to the sanctuary. But here is, unmistakably, a manual of religion, simple in its wording, direct in its meaning, profound in its significance, a book relevant to a normal human being all the time, and capable of lifting his ordinary life to the level of the heavenlies. It is not only that this Milieu is God's world : it is the real world as God reveals it to be.

This aspect of the cosmos is essential to Teilhard's experience and philosophy ; and though it permeates all his outlook and activities as their permanent atmosphere, it is more obvious in the last phase of his life when his own integration was complete and his circumstances gave him release from his hitherto incessant restlessness of effort. From the end of 1939 till his death on Easter Day in 1955 is a period of inward rather than outward growth—a harvesting of his many-sided activities and a storing up for the future of the results of his work which the authorities of his Society and Church would not allow him in his life-time to give to the world.

Not that these years were inactive : with the outbreak of war in Europe, he and Pierre Leroy the biologist and his friend in the Society were virtually imprisoned in Peking. The two men had met first in Teilhard's room when he was working at the Museum in Paris, and Leroy had been instructed by his superiors to join Licent in China where Teilhard joined him later in the same year. They met again in 1931 in Tientsin, and before the Yellow Cruise worked on the discoveries in Chou-Kou-Tien.[1] Now their scope was restricted. The Japanese invasion still controlled much of the country ; civil strife distracted much of it. It was not easy even to carry on his palaeontological researches, and surveillance was continuous and inhibiting. At first indeed his Superior charged him with being an evolutionist and therefore a communist, and told him to get back to France ; then he was put in charge of Chabanel Hall, a house for young recruits to the Society who had nothing in common with him ; finally he lodged with Leroy. There he said Mass at 7, smoked a cigarette with his colleague and talked for twenty minutes ; wrote down any ideas that had come to him during the night, and from 9 till 12 worked on his scientific reports ; rested for a short time in the early afternoon ; spent a couple of hours with Weidenreich in the laboratory ; went calling at 5 and came home punctually at 8. There was a small French community in the city and it gathered on Sundays at the house of old A. W. Grabau, the American geologist and doyen of all natural history in China ; Teilhard spent most of Sunday in the western hills, with a hammer and in shorts ; in the evenings he always started a discussion on some large subject of human interest. In addition, during the war years,

---

[1] *Letters from a Traveller,* p. 32.

he attended a small number of conferences—though these were very difficult to assemble—and delivered a very large number of lectures in English, some on literature ranging from Tolstoy and Dostoievski to Gide and Sartre, Camus and Graham Greene, others on religion from Troeltsch and Barth to Maréchal and Aldous Huxley, and philosophy from Nietzsche to Toynbee, from Darwin to John Dewey, and from Rostand to Nordenskiold. Unhappily we have no records of all the books that he handled and no relics of the treatment that he gave to them. But at least he used his enforced leisure widely and well. During it he achieved two discoveries, expressed as always in aphorisms—" La complexité engendre " (renders possible) " la conscience " and " La Réflexion croit " (self-consciousness involves faith in the ultra-human). These epitomise his concept of evolution.[1]

When at last the war in Japan was ended Teilhard was still unable to get away from Peking. China was in confusion ; the Japanese were still in possession, the rest of the world was too battered to concern itself ; he had to wait till March 1946 before he could get a plane to Shanghai, so to Hong Kong and thence to England for a couple of days and from Newhaven to Paris, to his room in 15 rue Monsieur. His books and papers, indeed almost all his possessions, were left in China and have never been recovered.

In Paris he lived as he said, a step at a time, delighted at first by the warmth of his welcome, glad to meet old friends like Paul Rivet of the Museum of Man whom he had met twenty-five years before in an attempt to persuade Boule to reopen contact with German scientists, or new like Nicolas Berdiaeff or Gabriel Marcel with whom he had a debate, indeed a duel, over their sharply contrasted views of Christianity. Conferences of this kind on a wide variety of subjects played a large part in his life : Cuénot lists some twenty of them between 1947 and 1951.[2]

In June 1947, when he had planned to visit South Africa

[1] For this account, cf. Cuénot, pp. 287–96.   [2] Pp. 316–17.

where Breuil had been living and to go with Barbour to meet Robert Broom and Raymond Dart at the scene of their great discoveries at Sterkfontein and Makapan, he was laid low with a serious heart attack and for many weeks was in great danger. His brother Joseph's house, Les Moulins, in his native Auvergne gave him back his health : [1] he was too tough to be an invalid : but thereafter he had to realise that there were limits to his powers. The lack of any definite work and the uncertainty of his own position added to his anxieties. His country might promote him to the grade of Officer in the Legion of Honour, but the Church paid no attention to his pleas for the recognition of Humanism and of the new knowledge and gave him no encouragement either as a scientist or as a priest. That winter was a time of great frustration, though he never complained or lost his faith and convictions. If he could publish his great book or obtain any regular teaching or research he might contribute to the critical issues of whose urgency he was increasingly certain. It was cruel to be dependent upon casual and largely disconnected engagements.

The next year, 1948, brought the question of his future to its decision. He received an invitation from Professor G. G. Simpson to join his group of experts in the American Museum in New York and do a spell of work with them. He was touched but obviously hesitant ; for he had no longer a primary concern with pure science. But America was, as he had described it, " his second home ", and at the end of February he crossed from Cherbourg to New York, met Weidenreich and von Koenigswald just appointed to Utrecht, and began to look for openings. The country was still recovering from the return of its " veterans " ; the shock of what had been done at Hiroshima, the beginnings of " an hysterical anti-communism ", and the plans for the United Nations distracted attention from less immediate interests.

[1] He was able to attend and speak at a meeting of the Geological Society of France on 1st December, cf. below, Chapter Six, p. 126.

His friends were welcoming but unsettled, and apart from private contacts with many individuals, a meeting with Barbour and a talk about his visit to South Africa, and a lecture on "The Trend and Significance of Human Socialisation" delivered in English to the Viking Foundation, he had a disappointing time. For himself he discovered a boredom with "the Past"; he could not revive his interest in geology except for the problem of the formation of the continents, and his vision of the future was hardly of the kind to inspire much public approval. Apart from a few young people his contacts with his own Church were not impressive; and he gained neither regular work nor any clear view of his future. But he had attained peace of soul and an inward experience of great value; and returned in June to Paris whence after a Conference he visited Britain in September.

Then after a holiday at Les Moulins he was told by his friend Rivet of the unanimous desire of the Collège de France that he should succeed to the professorship which Abbé Breuil had held for so many years. On this he was instructed by his Superiors that he must ask permission of the Vatican. So on 5th October he went to Rome, taking with him the final version of *Le Phénomène humain* for submission to the Holy Office. It was his first visit and he was a devout and humble man, but the letters quoted by Cuénot (pp. 325-6) give a vivid account of his impressions. "Rome has given and will give me no shock either aesthetic or spiritual : I am immunised against the past; and as for the picturesque there is nothing to compare with the grandeur of the East. It represents the earthly extremity of an arch which leads from man to what is above man." "Memories of childhood and a sense of the greatness of the Society." "I live with the 'Writers' (the archivists of the Society of Jesus) and others whose desire it is to say 'nothing to report'. The Curia reminds me of Chabanel." He was in fact completely isolated; given the conviction that his neighbours cared for life not as modern but only as eternal; and increasingly convinced that Christendom would never prevail until it had recognised, incorporated and "Christified" the Neo-Humanism with its evolutionary outlook and faith in the future. He was therefore not surprised when at the last possible moment he was forbidden to accept the chair at the Collège ; he was not permitted to publish *Le Milieu divin*, already officially recognised at Louvain ; nothing was decided about the *Phenomenon*, and this state of indecision was maintained from year to year. On his return he wrote a letter on 9th November expressing his growing sense of the need to dedicate the rest of his life " to the analysis and estimate of the biological value of the social phenomenon—that is of the reality of a degree of superhuman achievement " : the idea of the human community as at once the fulfilment and the Christification of mankind had become explicit for him. His life's work had reached its goal. His last letter to the great Lucien Cuénot,[1] on 17th May 1950, is the evidence of it, his election as a non-resident member of the Institut its recognition.

It was after this that Teilhard developed his connection with Torrès Bodet and Unesco, already begun in 1947 when he submitted to them his *Reflections on the Rights of Man*. This was published in 1949 and was followed in that year by a paper on a " Biologist's approach to the Idea of Democracy ". In July 1950 he sent a more important correspondence dealing with racial problems in which he strongly criticised the current ideas of the equality of races in favour of a view of their differences but complementarity and convergence. Groups hitherto isolated had developed independent skills and ways of life : to ensure the success of humanity these should not be standardised but as in a family be encouraged to make their own highest contribution. This was ignored even when he supplemented it in 1954 by protesting that he was not a " raciste " but regarded all races as " complementary and capable of synthesis in a world of sympathetic collaboration ". To Huxley he sent a memorandum in March 1951 advocating

[1] Cuénot, pp. 332–4.

the establishment of an Institute for Human Studies with a sketch of its possible organisation and objectives—an idea which Huxley was himself advocating.[1]

One further consequence of the action of the Vatican was suggested by a fellow-Jesuit, Father R. Jouve, who persuaded Teilhard to take definite and legal steps for the preservation of his writings with a view to their publication after his death. To secure that this could be done without disloyalty to his vows of obedience and poverty or defiance of ecclesiastical authority was a complicated task. But in 1951 just before Jouve's death the necessary permissions and support had been obtained. Teilhard could at least feel that if he would not live to see it his labours had not been in vain. The letter which he sent to Father Janssens in Rome on 12th October accepting the verdict of the hierarchy [2] is a noble witness to the quality of his mind and spirit.

In July of that year he had left France for London, met Barbour and joined him on his second expedition to South Africa to see the great sites of prehistoric sub-human or human remains, discovered and explored at Sterkfontein and Makapan which he had planned to visit in 1947.[3] Dr. Raymond Dart met them in his laboratory at Witwatersrand. Dr. J. T. Robinson of the Geological Service of Pretoria escorted them to the strongholds of Australopithecus, whose status was, and still is, keenly disputed. Dr. P. van Riet Lowe, head of the Archaeological Service of Johannesburg, took them to the Cave of Hearths and to grottoes where a more certainly human type had been recently found. They studied the importance of the very ancient " pebble industry ". Teilhard's interest in the evidence and his ingenuity in suggesting inter-

[1] Cf. Cuénot, pp. 368–9.
[2] Printed by P. Leroy, l.c. pp. 55–60, and cf. *Letters from a Traveller*, pp. 41–4. Its tone and language are entirely in keeping with the intimate letter sent to Barbour in April 1949.
[3] Barbour has given an account of their tour in *The World of Teilhard*, pp. 33–4.

pretations of it made it plain that though he was no longer primarily a palaeontologist he still kept a vivid affection for such studies—and that as he admitted, his health was much better on trek than in his study. Before leaving for South America he had visited Durban and seen the famous "living-fossil" fish caught at East London in 1937 and shown him by Miss Lattimer herself. He crossed by cargo-boat to Buenos Aires hoping to explore enough of South America to give him some evidence on the formation of continents. These plans proved impossible. But he met a German palaeontologist, Dr. O. Menghin, and learned from him of the search for early man in Patagonia. Instead of travelling north, as planned, by Valparaiso he went by Rio de Janeiro and Trinidad.

He was so attracted by the possibilities opened up by African researches that in 1953 he made a second visit, this time all alone, to the continent. He crossed direct from New York, eighteen days unbroken except by sight of Ascension and St. Helena, " a magnificent opportunity for reflection and work ",[1] to Cape Town where he inspected the new Rhodesian man found in the dunes at Hopefield. Then he began a long tour given in detail by Dr. Cuénot to Johannesburg and Pretoria, by plane in defiance of his doctor to Lusaka where he met Desmond Clark, and visited several sites which he described to Dr. Oakley, to the Victoria Falls, and so back in September to Bloemfontein and the south. His one disappointment was that he could not go on to Tanganyika and the Olduvai gorge where Leakey and his wife were working. As Cuénot points out, his visits to South Africa had much in common with those previously undertaken to Java. But their results upon his interpretation of man's ancestry were much more significant. We may question the validity of his sharp distinction between the Australopithecids and the Hominids, due in part to his desire to stress the difference of level between the Biosphere and the Noosphere : but he had no hesitation

---

[1] Cuénot, p. 399. He wrote *L'Étoffe de l'univers* on this voyage.

in accepting Africa south of the Sahara as the probable cradle of mankind.

Between these two visits he had fixed his permanent residence in New York. The Viking Foundation and its Director of Research, Paul Fejos, had been in touch with him ever since his paper to them in 1948 and was generous in its grants. This had now become the Wenner-Gren Foundation [1] for Anthropological Research with a house, 980 Park Avenue, where Teilhard was given a room. By the end of 1951 he had agreed to work for them as Research Associate in Palaeanthropology, and to combine this with his concern for the study of human evolution at its present stage and with the special task of relating scientific progress to religious experience and interpretation. His activities remained spasmodic and various, but his life was increasingly devoted to the deepening both of his understanding of the current problems and opportunities of human unification and of his insight into the nature and development of his own religious experience, alike individual and corporate. The two lines of study were intimately connected and were alike inspired by his basic conviction as to the unity between convergence and Christification. They arose out of the fusion of his desire for a new Anthropology, such as he had outlined in his original paper to the Viking Foundation in 1948 on human socialisation, with his increasing conviction that a purely cultural and humanistic study of mankind which ignored both the general course and interpretation of evolution and the specific influence of religion was totally inadequate. He devoted most of his energies in 1952 and 1953 to a correspondence and meetings in which he tried to convince representatives of the various branches of the subject, physiologists and sociologists, taxonomists and students of cultural development, that they should co-operate in developing a coordinated Anthropogenesis which would deal with the specific contribution of humanity to the progress of evolution and of

[1] Its founder, the great Swedish industrialist, died in November 1961.

its own future unification. In spite of encouragement from Huxley the conference in June 1952 was a sad disappointment, ending for him only in relative trivialities ; and the proposal for a committee for evolutionary humanism that autumn led only to further postponements. When in 1954 the plans for a conference in Paris brought him over to France in June, it gave him meetings with Jacques Rueff of the Institute, P. P. Grassé the biologist, J. Piveteau of the Sorbonne and Théodore Monod of the Museum at Dakar : but the visit was short and unhappy, and he was not himself able to come when the meetings took place in France in March 1955. Similarly a large symposium was suggested for June 1955 under the Wenner-Gren Foundation at which Arnold Toynbee would be present, and Teilhard looked for a full study of the Noo-sphere and an opportunity to propound his views of the Point Omega : but he had died before this assembled. His only achievement was a colloquy in October 1954 at Columbia University on the Unity of Human Knowledge at which he and Huxley with Étienne Gilson and seventy others were able to discuss for three days the possibility of an earthly ultra-human society—a prospect which Christians of all denominations refused to consider.

Alongside of these rather unsatisfying proposals was the opportunity of meeting many people of various eminence during visits to G. G. Simpson in New Mexico, to the cyclo-trons at Berkeley and to the *collenia* in Glacial Park, Montana. The genetic laboratories at Bar-harbour in Maine gave him a wide acquaintance with the North American continent,[1] and his work in New York introduced him to Margaret Mead the ethnologist and once again to Joseph Needham the bio-chemist and historian of Chinese science. His life was not empty of human interests even if the results led rather to the deepening of his own experience than to the practical advance-ment of the world-wide socialisation of which he dreamed. It is not easy to summarise these final activities, covering as

[1] Cf. Cuénot, pp. 416–22.

they did so wide a range and so large a synthesis. But we can look at the most important elements in his achievement and then study his own fullest account of " the Heart of the Matter ". When he died suddenly on the afternoon of Easter Day he had gone near to bringing both the Without and the Within of his life and thought into a fulfilment. His friend Father Leroy has described his last hours. His prayer that he might make a good end had been wonderfully granted.

The measure of his fulfilment can best be tested by the growth of his influence. In 1955 he had died in apparent loneliness and frustration. Already in 1952 the champions of orthodoxy had begun to publish their warnings against him. The United States was in no mood to receive or even understand his message.[1] His visits to Europe had led to little but disappointment. His work and writings were hardly known outside the *réseau teilhardien*, the network of men and women whose lives he had touched into fruition. It is no part of our purpose to deal here and now with his critics : representatives of them will be discussed in the last chapter of this book. But such a survey does not give any real impression of the speed and range of his impact. The number of books and articles devoted to him ; the societies and groups existing to promote the study and develop the application of his teaching ; the actual quality and quantity of his followers ; these are a better test. But the simplest evidence is probably found by citing a couple of individuals who illustrate the unity in diversity of his appeal. The diversity is the more important to remember since at present, as Dr. Barbour rightly observes, " he is so rapidly passing into history as a mystic and saint that people fail to think of him as a very human man."

Here are two examples of his significance. Barón Allard, the Belgian Catholic, artist, banker and international worker for peace who accompanied Queen Elisabeth of Belgium on

[1] Judging from some of the contributors to the recent American volume, *The World of Teilhard*, this is still the case : their world is not his.

her visit to China has lately published an outspoken and comprehensive volume, *Ferveur*, on the application of Christian doctrine to politics. In this he has collected a great anthology of quotations illuminating our present crisis. Teilhard is singled out for special citations on pages 63–4 from *L'Avenir de l'homme* in which he shows that the very struggle for survival which formerly forced man to war is or should be now forcing him to peace and the " progressive humanisation of humanity ". Allard also quotes Teilhard's *La Foi en la paix*,[1] to show his complete agreement with his friend, Pierre Girard, former Director of the Institut de Biologie Physico-Chimique in Paris in the task of directing and inspiring science into the fullest service of human welfare and unity.

The second example is Senator Roger Garaudy, the French Communist, Director of the Centre of Marxist Research in Paris, who has attended many conferences on Teilhard and spoken with evident admiration of his character and contribution to the social solidarity of mankind. In his recent book, *Perspectives de l'homme*, he discussed Existentialism, Catholic thought and Marxism as the principal systems of contemporary French philosophy. He pays much attention to Teilhard, objects to his insistence on the " within of things " as involving a rudimentary psychism, but acknowledges its points of contact with the Marxist doctrines of dialectic tension and inner compulsion. His obvious desire is to understand Teilhard's arguments, and he has a deep sympathy with his insistence upon the convergence and ultimate unity of mankind and with his practical proposals for its attainment.

Surely from samples like these we can appreciate how illusory was the suggestion of his failure. They attest, indeed would compel us to infer, the grandeur of the man who could produce such an impact, the variety of his gifts and the unity of his character. He embodied in himself one of his most famous phrases : in him as in the universe we recognise

---

[1] In *Cahiers du Mond nouveau*, January 1947, quoted by Allard on p. 125, following quotations from Girard on pp. 121–4.

l'union différenciée. Fortunately we have in his own sketch of his growth his illustration of that phrase.

Out of the various influences, the changing scenes, the adventures and frustrations of his life it is obvious that in Teilhard we can trace a singularly consistent growth of interest, appreciation and interpretation. Few men have been more active in the pursuit of a primary objective, few less favoured with the leisure and resources for continuous and systematic effort. Apart from his brothers and sisters and his attachment to his Church and Society he had no permanent anchorage, neither home, nor library, nor colleagues, and apart from his genius for friendship, his vigour of body and mind, and his indifference to his material surroundings, no special equipment for literary or scientific research. Yet the series of papers in which he expressed his knowledge and convictions shows a continuity of outlook and an increasing range of insight which would be remarkable in a man whose whole time had been devoted to the exposition of a " cosmic, human and Christ-centred " philosophy.

These three adjectives represent the three sections into which his last and most intimate Apologia, *Le Cœur de la matière*, is divided. Dated 15th August 1950 at Les Moulins, his brother's house in Auvergne, and circulated in cyclostyle to his friends it contains his own record of the growth and fulfilment of his thought and is indispensable for those who wish to know of what elements and in what stages his fullness of interpretation was fashioned.[1] On the page of Introduction he has set the words *Au cœur de la matière un cœur du monde, le cœur d'un dieu* and in it he claims only to be reporting a first-hand psychological experience—" how starting from an inherited spark of light the world during all my life and by means of all my life has gradually become entirely luminous from within."

[1] My own knowledge of this and of three other papers which mark critical stages in his development is due to a loan of her personal copies from Professor Dorothy Garrod.

" The Cosmic or Evolutionary " ; so he describes the first phase of his story—a phase characteristic of the great field-naturalists who have played so large a part in the study and interpretation of nature and the development of human intelligence. Like the first Greek philosophers Teilhard points to a sense of the oneness, wholeness and completeness of the universe, the *plénitude*, " *quelque unique suffisant et unique nécessaire* ", as the universal though sometime unrecognised human experience. This sense he regards as the guiding thread of his life.

But along with this and from the age of six or seven he had his own secret devotion to the concrete and particular, in his case to bits of iron which represented his " idols " a ploughshare, the top of a metal pillar, a piece of a shell from the range.[1] Outwardly affectionate and devout his real life centred in these sacred objects which made the " absolute " tangible, and individualised the universal. Some such attachment, if it may easily degenerate into the collecting mania, is an essential attribute for the naturalist : like Adam he must inspect the stuff of the world and name its flora and fauna : he must gain a sense of discrimination and order and relatedness, if plurality is to find its meaning in unity. Teilhard born in Auvergne with a father interested in the country and its creatures started with geology (surely the proper basis), went on to the fossils, the plants and insects, and so in his later school-days to the elementary physics of the end of the last century. From a lump of iron to the Point Omega is a long road ; but from the mineral and solid to the new and the rare, from the fixed pieces of a puzzle given at the creation to the pageant of life as it develops and becomes ever more complex, that was a journey that took him twenty years.

It was at Hastings that there came to him his knowledge of evolution, and in the sunlight on the Downs his vision of the living world, of the biosphere enveloping and now increas-

[1] So P. Leroy, *Teilhard de Chardin, tel que je l'ai connu*, p. 11 ; *Letters*, p. 20.

ingly shaping the earth, of Bergson's vision of creation as a
continuous and cosmic reality, and of *duration*, space-time, as
the background of a universe continually proceeding from the
predominantly material to the psychic and the personal, from
the sphere of life to the sphere of mind. So the old picture of
dualities, Matter and Energy, Body and Soul, Without and
Within, of static elements fixed in a permanent pattern, of a
kaleidoscope in which nothing was new or unprecedented,
had to be rejected and replaced. To do so was as Teilhard
admits a life's task. Yet for him the change was rapid and
relatively easy ; and the problems, as he can claim, have been
resolved.

" The Human or the Converging " : that is the heading
of his second section when he passes from the scientific and
evolutionary to the world of thought, of intelligence and of
man's conscious control of process. He begins by admitting
how difficult it was for him to abandon his childhood sense of
the solidity and permanence of the earth in comparison with
the relative instability of the human organism, and of the scale
of the universe as compared with that of individual and transient men. Nevertheless he was cured of this as he came to
experience and to explain the reality of the noosphere or realm
of mind ; and here his sense of human solidarity arose from
his direct experience in the army at Verdun. Like others of
us under similar ordeal he realised and perceived as with an
extra sense the organic solidarity of the great community of
soldiery.[1] This led him to compare the " surface-tension " of
the noosphere to the phenomena of convergence and sym-
biosis where unity of a new kind between elements seemingly
diverse achieves and sustains activities of indisputable efficacy.
For thirty years since this experience Teilhard continued to

---

[1] I may perhaps refer to my own account of a similar experience on the
night before our attack at Oppy Wood in April 1917. Thirty-five years
ago I urged in a course of lectures at Harvard that this sort of Group
coherence should be examined by psychological research. Cf. *The Creator
Spirit* (London, 1927), pp. 200–1.

strengthen his understanding of convergence—the belief that living matter, beneath the apparent inertia of its surface, possesses a planet-wide power which if studied and directed might accomplish the unification of mankind. The increase of technical skills and of social interdependence have made such a development of the noosphere indispensable. Reflection and unanimisation may seem remote to us in view of our present hatreds and fears, but " zoologically and biologically speaking Man, at last discerned in the cosmic integrity of his course, is still only at an embryonic stage of it : beyond there already stands out an abundant fringe of ultra-human." " So the bit of iron of my early days is long ago forgotten. But in its place, in the form of Point Omega, there is the Stability of the Universe which I now hold gathered together into a single indestructible centre that I can love."

" The Christic or Central " : so he defines the third phase of his exposition. As a preface to it he claims that with his sense of wholeness even if he had been an unbeliever his own impulses would have led him to the summit which he has already described ; he even conjectures that by a purely rational appreciation of the character of the cosmic process he would have recognised in an incarnate Deity the only appropriate centre and fulfilment of the biopsychological development achieved by the evolution of a living and intelligent community. " To be a Man I might have been obliged to make myself a Christian."

This is, of course, speculation : he was born of a fully Catholic stock with the result that alongside the free evolution of the cosmic awareness described in the two first sections of this paper, another process was constantly at work in him—a sense of Christ which must be described from infancy onwards. For at first these two, the Cosmic and the Christic seemed quite independent. It was only after much time and effort that he came to realise, by way of study of the Human, their linkage, convergence and finally basic identity.

But the contact with God did not yet amount to love, it

was a conjecture, an aspiration—with all the world between it and him. To set it alight there was need of a spark such as fell on him from his mother's contact with Christian mysticism. This saved him from the usual difficulty of imagining the possibility of a superhuman love ; and by whatever means gave him a constant ability to approach God as a " supreme someone " and a capacity alongside his cosmic awareness to experience a love of the unseen—a " taste of heaven " which both sustained his native taste for earth and could universalise and materialise his concept of divine love. He admits in a note that this love of the unseen was nourished by the influence of the feminine. Absorbed with his mother's milk there flowed into him a sense of the supernatural Divine alongside of his sense of natural wholeness : each of them claimed the whole of him : neither could destroy the other : inevitably the supernatural, less primitive and genetically speaking more external, was assimilated by the other, the Divine was adjusted to the Evolutionary, that is—to the psychological law of his nature which could only adore what arose from the tangible and resistant. God could only find a place if he was represented by a natural symbol.

In this respect his progress was promoted by the fact that his mother's God was for him as for her the Incarnate Word. Starting from this principle of the humanity of Jesus a first contact was established between the Christian and the pagan halves of his basic self—a contact precisely at the point of his previously mentioned difficulty, the solidity (" consistance ") of the human. Before he could fully adore the Christ, he must first " consolidate " him, and this was effected (" ludicrous as this may appear ") by the influence of a devotional exercise in which his mother had trained him (though she never realised how much his insatiable concern with the organic aspect of the cosmos would affect him), the cult of the Heart of Jesus.

On this side of his development, as on the parallel case of his iron fetishes as focusing and representing for him the wonder and wholeness of nature, he is smilingly apologetic for the limitations and unsightliness of his sacred object. The cult of the Sacred Heart both in its emphasis upon sin and reparation and in its iconography and anatomy, he recognises as strangely limited both in itself and in its present-day meaning ; the liturgy ought not to be sin-obsessed nor the symbolism so liable to offend. Yet for him, though neither the objective nor the instrument attracted him, this concentration produced an astonishing liberation ; the whole physical and spiritual reality of Christ manifested itself in a concrete object in which all limiting particularity vanished away. The fullness of Christ like the fullness of the material world dominated him in a similar fashion. The supreme synthesis of the divine and the carnal, of the Upward and the Onward began to work itself out. In each case the material object, the lump of iron or the sacred heart, was, so to say, the explosive event by which the whole level represented by it became luminous ; the particular exploded into the universal. From this symbol the divine became an energy, all-pervading, transforming, universalising, breaking out into the cosmic milieu within which, on another side of his nature, he was already becoming established. " In my pagan self the universe personalised itself by convergence, in my Christian a Person (the Christ) universalised Himself by radiance."

But this first experience of the universal Christ involved long periods of conflict and of progress. For Teilhard as for most traditional Christians the antithesis between the two worlds was emphasised by the doctrines, the ethics and the practices of the Church. God even for the mystics was " in heaven " and between Him and the world a great gulf was fixed. Achievement of the spiritual must surely involve detachment from the material. There might be for Teilhard with his love of the natural world a conviction cutting across this contrast that matter was the womb of consciousness, and that consciousness developed up to and beyond the human level : but this gave rise to a new contrast between the transcendant and the indwelling deity, between the Upward and the Onward, the Cosmic and the Christic.

His account of this struggle, typical as it surely is of many a young naturalist, is worth reporting. " The first signs of it I recollect in my years at school, in the pathetic effort to reconcile with my love of nature the appeal (too narrow no doubt) of the ' Imitation ' the text of which was the substance of my morning prayers. Later on as a student in Jersey I seriously considered the total renunciation of my beloved geology in order to devote myself to the pursuits called ' supernatural '. That I was not wrecked at that moment was due to the robust common sense of the Master of the novices [1] who took occasion to assure me that the God of the Cross cared for my natural growth as well as for my sanctification. He didn't explain how or why : but it was enough to leave me with the two ends of the thread in my hands. So I found myself saved. Bit by bit, under the synthetic influence of experience, detachment and attachment, renunciation and development began to join up automatically in a sort of meeting-point of which in 1927 I gave the explanation in the first chapter of the *Milieu divin*." But he is constrained to add, " The explanation is not always practicable. Even to-day I have not finished exploring the dangers to which the man is exposed when by inner constraint he sees himself compelled to leave the beaten track of traditional discipline, now for him sub-human, and look for a road to heaven whereon the whole energy of Matter and Flesh can pass into the birth of Spirit." [2]

To Christify matter, " *atteindre le ciel par achèvement de la terre* "—this he defines as the goal of his inner life ; and the progress towards it was marked by two " *grands souffles* ", *La Messe sur le monde* of 1924 and *Le Milieu divin* of 1927. Looking back on them he can now realise first that all the

[1] According to Grenet, l.c. p. 61, he was Père Paul Troussard, who also gave great help to Valensin, cf. *A. Valensin*, p. 33.

[2] In this connection he refers not only to *Le Milieu* but to an essay of 1919, " The Mantle of Elijah ", written in Jersey.

essential elements of his Christic vision were then already fixed
and then that at a definite point his picture of the Universe
became still vague and unstable. Though he was fully aware
of an organic life diffused throughout the world and rendering
it transparent to the Christ, he had not in 1930 arrived at the
fact of universal convergence with its consequences, the emergence of conscience from complexity, the coming-together of
the branches of mankind, the existence of the Omega point as
the fulfilment of the birth of mind—all this was not yet evident : plurality was not yet orderly. For the next twenty
years it was his work and his joy to see the pattern of it taking
shape, in the spiral energy of the Incarnate Christ expanding
continually to his view, the " Évoluteur " in the evolving
cosmos, the universal Christ whose heart coincides with the
heart of *la matière amorisée*,[1] matter now realised as integrated
by love.

Yet this coincidence had its special danger for the evolving
individual. Either following the eastern and pagan way he
might allow his existence to become dissolved into the de-
humanised and universal, or on the contrary he might detach
it and slip away into the retrograde and material. One day
he perceived that convergence supplied a third way ; that out
of the real oneness of the cosmic, the human and the Christic
there emerged a new sphere, the Centric, in which the multiple
contradictions which make up the misery of our existence
tended to disappear.

The first effect of this unity was almost overwhelming.
Would not such totalisation involve monotony, such unity a
mechanisation from which there is no escape ? Yet after this
nightmare came the dawn of a new sense of convergence and
movement in which the bonds that support us tend to merge
into the attraction which impels our ego forwards. The elements now united are not rearranged, but personalised ; as

[1] This appears to be the last of his own specially adopted words. It
occurs in the manuscript *Lexique de mes termes*, reproduced in Cuénot,
p. 353, and dated 1951.

love expands matter is integrated into spirit. The universe itself becomes potentially lovely and loving, not static and kaleidoscopic but evolutionary, co-operative and Christ-centred. "From the view-point of convergent evolution, whither I have been led, confirmed by sixty years of experience and reflection, the entire cosmic story comes back basically to a single vast process of arrangement, the mechanism of which, making use of large numbers and the play of chance,[1] releases at each instant a certain amount of suffering (failures, discomposure, death). Now through the accession of Christ to the point Omega it is precisely the two aspects, constructive and destructive, of this operation that are invaded and penetrated by a flood of unitive power. Personalised simultaneously and at a single stroke, in its developments that place us centrally for Christ as well as in its diminutions that put us out of centre for Him, cosmogenesis, even in its most unrelenting and most obscure determinisms, abruptly takes the form of a limitless contact with a supreme pole of attraction and completion. A wave of love, suddenly sent forth, spreads over the whole surface of the world, and throughout its depths, not just as if it were some super-added warmth or perfume, but as a basic principle destined to change everything, to assimilate everything, to replace everything." So (to paraphrase his closing sentence) his whole being was exalted to discover the Universe as in a rapture in which all effort of study, all desire to create and all acceptance of suffering combine to press onward to the height from which to search out the future and see the triumph of God. He concludes with adoration and prayer.

---

[1] This phrase already employed by him must surely be a product of his talks with Huxley.

CHAPTER SIX

TEILHARD AND HUMAN ORIGINS

IT IS OF COURSE IMPROPER for anyone except an expert to attempt the discussion of Teilhard's standing and work as a palaeontologist or to estimate in any detail his contributions to our knowledge of human evolution. We others can only take the verdict of his colleagues. We shall find them almost unanimous in stating that for his first-hand study of the whole subject and still more for his insight and interpretative skill he stood (as one of them put it to me) " right at the top ". Had he been given professional status and a staff on the academic scale, he would plainly have made a great name for himself in science. Those of us who are too ignorant to appreciate the problems of first-hand research in palaeontology can at least see how eagerly and discerningly he gathered material ; how carefully he weighed and tested its significance ; how resolutely he followed up all relevant discoveries ; and how till his last days he not only remained open to new evidence but was quick to recognise the need for restatement of previously held conclusions and anticipate the future course towards which the fresh facts were pointing.

Though by the end of his life he had an almost unrivalled knowledge of the world-wide field—Western Europe ; Chou-Kou-Tien and China ; India from Kashmir to the Irrawaddy and so to Java ; and finally all the chief sites in Africa, he was never able to combine his explorations into a single monograph. But thanks to the care and wisdom of the Committee responsible for the posthumous publication of his works we have got seventeen of his papers produced between 1913 and 1954 collected in the volume *L'Apparition de l'homme* in 1956 as the second of the five. These, although their selection must have been difficult since they were never planned as a series, yet give a tolerably adequate sequence of his records and enable us to appreciate the range and development of his researches and the growth of his powers of interpretation. The book has an excellent introduction by Dr. N. M. Wildiers, a very wise exposition of Teilhard's philosophy of evolution and of the present illustration of it by the development of his thought in this sequence ranging from his first sketch of prehistory [1] to the final essay on the uniqueness of man.

He had started as we have seen with Eoanthropus, and though doubts of its significance and even its authenticity must have arisen as soon as he faced Boule's scepticism, he had at least been introduced vividly to the idea that our ancestors went back beyond the cave-decorators of Aurignac or the flint-chippers of Saint-Acheule. But in France it was obviously with these that he would begin his serious palaeontology. It was in 1913 that he joined a party led by the Bavarian priest Hugo Obermaier, expert on the Spanish grottoes and caves and author of *Fossil Man in Spain*, and met Nels C. Nelson the American scientist whom he met again in China in 1926 and on his first visit to the United States in 1931, and Miles Burkitt, then a young student on his first expedition. Breuil, holding his first post at the Institut, was with them, and already absorbed in the art and culture of prehistoric Europe ; and they were assembled for a dig at Castillo, the most interesting and inclusive of caves.

Teilhard was himself a naturalist rather than a historian. His work had been with fossils rather than artifacts, with the plants of Fairlight and the animals whose bones he was studying for his doctorate. Even in Rome, thirty-five years later, he was to confess that the art and architecture of the Holy

[1] Cf. above, Chapter Two, especially pp. 49, 50.

City made no deep impression on him. So in his anthropology it is with man as a creature, his place in the scheme of things and his structure and development rather than with the quality and dating of his manufactures that in his earlier days he was primarily concerned.

While he was working with Boule on his thesis the Museum received a number of mammalian fossils from a Jesuit naturalist in China, Émile Licent, who had set up a centre at Tientsin for his collections. Boule handed these over for study to Teilhard who received in consequence an invitation to go to China. This he accepted for one year in 1923. He went out twice with Barbour to Sang Kan-ho. Then Licent, who was not a geologist, arranged for his visitor to accompany him to the Ordos, a plateau in Western Mongolia which had been visited by C. H. Pope of the Central Asiatic Expedition in 1922. Here in two separate stations they found clear evidence of palaeolithic man. Teilhard reported this to Boule and Breuil, and the first proof of prehistoric humanity east of the Yenisei was duly announced. This, as Leroy noted, was the prelude to his subsequent work.[1]

It was not till after his departure that B. Bohlin and Davidson Black made known in 1927 their discovery of a tooth and jaw at Chou-Kou-Tien [2] and announced Sinanthropus to the world. On his return Teilhard found his first absorbing research. Then as always he gave the publicity to his Chinese colleagues and to Franz Weidenreich, Head of the Survey, but both then and still more when the Japanese invasion made the work precarious and unsafe he was obviously responsible for inspiring enthusiasm, insisting upon persistence, and directing the gathering of material. As this was apparently removed during the war by the Japanese and despatched to

[1] An adequate and short account of the journeys and work of Teilhard in China, 1923–45, is given by Paul Grenet in *Teilhard de Chardin* (Seghers, Paris, 1961). For this one cf. P. Leroy, p. 28.

[2] Andersson and O. Zdansky of Uppsala had already found the locality.

Japan on a ship that was lost at sea, and as others were mainly responsible for signing the Reports on their discoveries, his large share in the very successful investigation of Chou-Kou-Tien has hardly been mentioned or acknowledged.

In 1935 after three months in France he sailed in September to Bombay. His visit to India was in response to an invitation from America to join his friend Helmut de Terra on a small expedition to Kashmir. He was not enthusiastic about the prospect ; for he was beginning to be more concerned with the present and future of mankind than with the past, and had never been specially fascinated with the prehistory of *Homo sapiens*. But after writing *La Découverte du passé* on the voyage he went on to Lahore and the Himalayas and so recovered his eagerness for exploration. At Rawalpindi he met T. T. Paterson, then a young lecturer in Cambridge, and at Srinagar they joined de Terra and found evidence of two periods of prehistoric man not previously noted. Near the Indus they found fossil remains of anthropoids, and a rich palaeolithic industry on two levels. After a month in this area and a fortnight around Sind he ended his work with de Terra by a fortnight on the river Narbada up to Hoshangabad where he studied the famous paintings and decided that they were much older than the commonly accepted date. On 15th December he went on to Calcutta and thence to Batavia to see von Koenigswald by way of Rangoon and Singapore. The Indian visit encouraged him to say in several letters [1] that he thought their work had given a good start to the prehistory of the sub-continent : and de Terra has testified to his unique contribution to its success ; " he combined great clarity of thought and a vast store of knowledge with an intuition that hardly ever failed and enabled him to recognise the links between the differing levels of our discoveries ".[2]

When he returned to Burma in the spring of 1938 he

---

[1] *Letters from a Traveller*, pp. 188–200.
[2] Cf. his article in *Revue Teilhard*, 6, p. 5.

spent three months with de Terra and Movius on the Irrawaddy, went down to Mandalay, found new evidence of palaeolithic work there and felt that the development of early man in the far-east of Asia was reasonably plain. On 24th March the party left Rangoon for Singapore and Java where Teilhard fulfilled an expectation by finding *Stegodon* bones in the valley of the Solo. Von Koenigswald had fresh material to show, including the " baby skull " in the Trinil area and at Sangaran and in the south of the island. After little more than a fortnight he returned to Singapore, saw Collings, who had made important finds in the south of Penang, and so went on to China. His two brief visits were highly important in enabling him to complete a first-hand know-ledge of the haunts and remains of Pithecanthropus and con-sider the problem of his origin in relation to the whole palaeontology of Malaya, Burma and south-east China. He was in a unique position to link up Trinil with Chou-Kou-Tien.[1]

His last direct contribution to this field was in 1947 when, after his illness which prevented his journey to Africa, he pre-sented on 1st December to the Geological Society of France a cast of the famous jaw of *Meganthropus palaeojavanicus* found by von Koenigswald at Sangiran in 1941 and gave his own opinion upon it which differed in some respects from that of its discoverer and of Weidenreich.[2] Cuénot is fully justified in his claim that though the professional workers naturally received the fame, Teilhard's flair for the value and his fore-sight as to the sequels of their work disclose his knowledge of it and his estimate of its significance. It is largely due to him that the antiquity and the long-term importance of Pithecanthropus and of the artifacts and use of fire in his cave have been so generally admitted,[3] and that attention was

[1] Cf. Cuénot, pp. 248–50.

[2] Cf. Summary of the Meetings of the Society, 1947, pp. 309–10.

[3] Detailed examination and concrete instances of Teilhard's " modesty " and contributions are given by Grenet, l.c. pp. 99, 106.

directed towards the full exploration of Asia. It is good to know that his researches into prehistory, the exploration of Chou-Kou-Tien and the opening up of new sites have been vigorously continued.[1]

After the war he had not been long in Paris when he received an invitation from Abbé Breuil to pay a visit to South Africa. Breuil had himself left France in 1942 for Johannesburg and had gone to the newly discovered prehistoric sites in the Transvaal and had published a book with an introduction by Field-Marshal Smuts, then Prime Minister. Smuts, on Breuil's suggestion, now urged Teilhard to give them his expert advice upon the rich collections of material from Taungs, Makapan and Sterkfontein.[2] Though his heart attack upset his plans then, his mind was fixed on the project and he had made full preparations for it. So in 1951 he was able to embark on his last adventure—the African studies which gave him his final clue to the story of our inheritance. He who had devoted himself to Asia and done much to establish its claim to be the cradle of the first hominid, was yet ready from the beginning to admit the significance of Australopithecus and the labours of Dart and Broom, to visit and applaud them ; and at the same time after doing so to recognise that the Leakeys' find at Kanam was a new and revolutionary contribution to the earliest record. Pithecanthropus though differing in degree from the man of Heidelberg and generically from *Homo sapiens* was plainly human. Alike in physical qualities and by the evidence of his tool-making and use of hearths he had passed the barrier between man and ape. But Australopithecus was different. By the size and shape of his brain-case with its nuchal crest and scanty chin he was evidently nearer to the apes, and if his teeth were closer to the human his limbs and gait were less plainly upright. Nor was there

[1] Reports of them can be found in " China Reconstructs ", in the *Peking Review*, and other journals, as well as in Chinese scientific publications. Cf. also Cuénot, p. 207.

[2] Cf. *Letters from a Traveller*, p. 292, and above, Chapter Three.

evidence of stone-tools or any mastery of fire. Teilhard put him on the animal side of the gap. But this did not prevent him from recognising his place in the pedigree nor from eagerness to see fuller evidence both of his structure and of his capabilities.

Very striking is the testimony that Dr. Dart and his advocate Robert Ardrey pay to the veteran Jesuit whom they regarded as Asiatic in his sympathies and liable to be indifferent if not hostile to their theories. Here is the record : [1] " Many a European scientist had invested his thought and his life in *Pithecanthropus erectus* and Peking Man and could not part easily with the proposition that mankind had arisen in Asia. But then a great French Jesuit philosopher and anthropologist emerged on the African scene. Père Teilhard de Chardin had done most of his work in the Far East, and when he returned as a frail old man he insisted on visiting South Africa and viewing all the Australopithecine sites. And in 1952 he gave a definitive report to the New York Academy of Science. He placed the era of the Australopithecines as the Villafranchian, that is between five hundred thousand and a million years ago. He regarded them as an autonomous zoological group, neither ape nor man, that to a large extent formed a bridge between the two. And he concluded : ' Their late Tertiary occurrence in Africa offers an additional argument that this continent was the main birthplace of the human group '." That Teilhard was prevented from his first-planned visit in 1947 by his heart-attack postponed his verdict for five years, but his readiness to revise his whole previous conclusions and to accept at once the prima-facie case for Africa south of the Sahara as the site of Eden is sufficient proof not only of his greatness but of his insight. Barbour's evidence in his article " Ape or Man " in 1949 must of course have been well known to him, for they had discussed it at Les Moulins in 1950 ; but first-hand experience, when the postponed journey took place, was needed before he could express his opinion. This

[1] *African Genesis*, by R. Ardrey, 1961, pp. 178–9.

was given in the *Revue des Questions Scientifiques* in January 1955.[1]

He concludes that the Australopithecines are a widely distributed and variable group covering an area from the Vaal to the Limpopo shortly before Man or true hominids appeared. Most of them were relatively small like *Australopithecus africanus* ; but large forms also existed : they are humanoid but not yet more, whereas the Pithecanthropi, a little more recent, are " already though only just human ".[2] Each of these two early stages represent distinct and easily recognisable types.

He decides that their individuality as a sub-human group makes it a mistake to regard them as having given birth to man or being on the direct line to him though they contribute to it in three respects.[3]

After his second visit he expressed his belief that man's origin may have involved an early division into two lines of roughly parallel development, one in Africa the other in Asia, each line containing three stages—Australopithecine, Pithecanthropic and Neanderthalean. This would be an example of the parallel development so familiar in the animal life of Marsupials in Australia and Placentals in the Old World. It would presumably revive the old controversy aroused and only partly met in the *Phenomenon*, as between the advocates of a single family or a single race as the immediate ancestors of man, on which he had declined to be dogmatic. As regards Australopithecus he disagrees with Robinson and Oakley in their belief that the man-ape and the true man lived side by side. He also continues to affirm that Australopithecus had no industry.[4]

This latter insistence he never seems to have discussed in relation to the evidence that the use of weapons is indicated by the number of baboon heads found in the deposits and

[1] Printed in *L'Apparition de l'homme*, pp. 277–91—there following upon reprints of his papers reporting on his own two journeys, pp. 245 ff.

[2] From his report of 1952.

[3] Cf. *L'Apparition*, pp. 254–5 and 281–2.

[4] *L'Apparition*, p. 273.

showing depressed fractures of the parietal bones of an identical position and shape. Barbour in his report already mentioned had explicitly referred to the theory that bones of other animals were appropriately selected and shaped to inflict these wounds and had claimed that this would show intelligence and skill. Sir Wilfrid le Gros Clark writing his *Fossil Evidence for Human Evolution* in the same year as Teilhard's report mentions this possibility and commends it for further examination.[1] But Teilhard so far as is known says nothing about it. This may be due to the fact that on his visits he saw little of Dr. Dart[2] who is the chief advocate of the regular use of bone tools and weapons at this level of development.

Of the acute controversy aroused over this crucial issue Mr. Ardrey's book, *African Genesis*, already mentioned, gives a long and detailed record. It is difficult not to feel that the case is very strong—indeed unanswerable ; and most of us know from experience how ready even famous scientists can be to turn a blind eye upon data which do not fit into their preconceptions. Most of the older naturalists are still slow to accept the evidence that aesthetic, intellectual and even moral values have been evolved and are in rudiments manifested very long before any sort of human stock existed. Comparative psychology (as contrasted with anthropomorphic interpretations of subhuman behaviour) is a recent field of study ; and too many of us are still accustomed to explain animal reactions and activities in terms of human functioning and motive. But if we admit the tool-making and skill of the Australopithecids it is not necessary to accept the conclusions as to our inheritance which Ardrey in his very readable and challenging book proclaims. If Australopithecus was a flesh-eater and a killer whose weapon was his fetish it does not follow that this element in his character has descended to us and is the clue to man's love of violence and arms-races. If we are directly descended from this phylum (which is still

[1] Cf. also K. P. Oakley, "The Earliest Tool-makers", *Antiquity*, xxx, pp. 4–8.   [2] Cf. *Letters from a Traveller*, p. 309.

not certain) killing was not the only occupation of its life. Ardrey admits that he is ignoring " the beginnings of sexual activity as an all-year-round affair and the consequent beginnings of the primate family " [1] which some of us believe to be basic to our human condition. He pays no heed to the revolutionary changes which agriculture, stock-breeding and village life have involved. And, though it is rude to suggest it, he is too ready to estimate human conduct from the standpoint of the gangsters of Chicago and the gunmen of the Wild West. In any case, he never recognises that this carnivorous warrior accomplished nothing but his own extinction.

However this may be, Dr. Leakey's paper on the First Men given to the British Academy on 7th October 1959 gives clear evidence that in the lowest bed of the Olduvai Gorge were tools of a simple type older than any known Chellean culture, pebble-tools, a hammer stone and flakes with the bones of small animals and birds broken up and evidently food. These were found along with the almost complete skull of a definitely Australopithecine type which he named *Zinjanthropus Boisei*. This he regarded as certainly the maker of the tools, a vegetable-feeder, now become carnivorous, and coeval with and akin to the ape-men of Dr. Dart. He is probably the ancestor of the culture which succeeded the Oldowan in Bed 2 of Olduvai, and is fully entitled to rank as Man. [2] Dr. Oakley has approved this interpretation of the find and regards it as highly important. He has recently assigned the Australopithecid or small-brained men to a period about a million years ago, the large-brained Pithecanthropids and Neanderthalers to half a million, and modern man to about 40,000. [3]

Until the evidence of Olduvai has been fully explored and interpreted the question of the precise relationship of the small-brained and stooping Australopithecids to the large-skulled and fully upright Pithecanthropids cannot be fully

[1] L.c. p. 317.   [2] Cf. *Antiquity*, XXXIII, pp. 235–7, 1959.
[3] Address to British Association, 4th September 1961 (cf. *The Times*, 5th September).

decided. At present the two seem to overlap in date ; and if
so it may be that though both proceed from a common ancestor
they are cousins rather than father and son, and one of them
more strongly simian than the other. At Olduvai it seems
probable that the lowest stratum has yielded relics hominoid
rather than human ; and, if so, higher strata in the gorge may
indicate how and when true man emerged. Teilhard evidently
felt that the Transvaal group of species were ape-men, whether
or no they were in the direct line of man's descent. He did
not, as we have noted, usually lay much stress upon sudden
and large-scale mutations, but he explicitly states his conviction that recognisable and indeed easily distinguished levels
of development are characteristic of our pedigree ; that in
any case some intermediate or sub-human forms lie behind
our Javan and Pekinese ancestors ; and that Africa and probably the Kenya-Tanganyika area is our most probable
birthplace.[1]

As to what constitutes the new level that separates ape
from man he has no hesitation. It is not the structure of the
brain-case, still less the teeth or the upright posture. It is not
the tool-making which led Bergson to name man *Homo
faber*[2] nor the use of fire, nor the sexual change which has
transformed the annual breeding-season into the life of the
family. It is, and this he regards as his crucial discovery, the
attainment of self-consciousness and the consequent " noosphere " or realm of reflection which others have called the
attainment of a " self of contemplation " as opposed to that
of " enjoyment ". Man has become aware of his own solitariness and of the world as over against himself ; he can
realise himself as living in space and time, capable of recalling
the past in memory and of seeing himself as acting in a planned
sequence of events and upon an interpreted environment. He

[1] *L'Apparition*, p. 279, etc.
[2] Yet " systematic tool-making, even of the simplest kind, indicates
foresight based on memory and it indicates tradition ", K. P. Oakley,
Antiquity, xxx, p. 5.

is aware both of the varied plurality of things and people, and of the essential unity of the world to which he belongs but in which he is alone, and in a measure free and responsible. He can experience worship and dereliction, fulfilment and guilt ; and a wholly new sense both of individuality and of community is now part of his inheritance. Imagination and foresight, repentance and fear take on a new meaning for him. He lives in an environment which he does not merely accept but can manipulate and understand and control. " Man is ", as Teilhard puts it, " not only a being who knows but a being who knows that he knows." [1]

This to Teilhard as to his friends from Le Roy to Huxley is a break, an emergence, as distinct as that of life itself, a break within the continuity of evolution but manifesting the novelty of a fresh and unique level of existence. Man is still physically an animal ; the stuff of his being is contained within the creative process ; but the emergence like that of water from hydrogen and oxygen which constitutes humanity is not merely a change of pattern but the arrival of a new and unprecedented entity ; and by it the world has entered upon a new phase of its development.

For Teilhard this new development was essentially religious in its true sense. Man attained an awareness not only of the oneness of his world but of its mystery—that is of its disclosure of meaning, worth and personal or superpersonal quality. This awareness, at first wholly undefined, took shape gradually as it was focused upon certain elements in his own experience which evoked in him awe and dread, wonder and rapture, curiosity and exploration, the desire to describe and explain. It became associated with events in his own life and circumstances, with places and objects, with appropriate behaviour and ritual. It compelled ideas as to the meaning and origin of life and of the world, of his own nature and functioning, of pleasures and pains and of social relationships, loyalties and hates. It constrained certain patterns of behaviour and

[1] *L'Apparition*, p. 314.

standards of conduct. It pointed as Teilhard put it " onward and upward."

The whole development was accompanied and conditioned by the changes in man's own activities and way of living. The growing of crops and the taming of animals necessitated a measure of co-operation between families, and the village with its co-operative distribution of function, its relative security of life and food, and its opportunities for leisure, for folk-tales and arts and social ritual, for the training of the young, and the practice of individual skills. Numbers increased, tribes and tribal associations arose ; settlements became larger, homes more permanent, transport more necessary. The wheel and the baggage animal changed the area and relationships of life. Money as a medium of exchange enlarged barter into trade. Civilisation and the city grew up side by side especially in China, India and Mesopotamia by the end of the neolithic age. Changes of climate and the consequent need for adaptability introduced struggles less crude than those of hunting and fighting, and put a high premium upon individual ingenuity and corporate stability. Ideas of law and order in the community and in the natural world, methods of regulation and government, speculations as to the riddles of death and birth, the origin and rhythm of the world, the experiencing of happiness and sorrow, of reward and retribution, of worship and shame began to open up the whole content and meaning of life. Evolution could become conscious, recognisable and open to control.

It is appropriate that after his survey of the probable origin and course of human evolution, the book in which his sixteen papers are collected should end with a longer and more general discussion of the basic question how far this process is simply a perpetuation of certain somatic and psychic qualities which combine and recombine but remain essentially similar and fixed. Rejecting this kaleidoscopic view of the world, and maintaining the reality of its onward and upward movement, we must still ask what evidence is there of the " singularity " of the human species. Is man, as Dr. Dart and Mr. Ardrey suggest, fundamentally the same old victim of an amity-enmity complex whose quality is determined mainly if not wholly by his basic requirements of fighting and territory ; or more generally is he as Marcellin Boule put it " an animal more astute perhaps, but from the standpoint of the biologist just as much an animal as all the rest " ? [1] On the other hand, if as Sir Julian Huxley had affirmed " Man stands alone " how can we vindicate and explain this uniqueness ? In almost his last considerable paper written in 1954 and printed at the time of his death Teilhard set himself to attempt an answer.

In doing so he was resuming the letter which Dr. Cuénot records [2] as written to Huxley on 27th February 1953. There he was discussing the fact that he, Teilhard, Huxley and Sir Charles Galton Darwin in his book *The Next Million Years* were very close together in their main line of thought. All three observe that mankind is being crowded in upon itself and entangled in a network of cultures and creeds which display different types of animal ancestry. " Where we differ in our estimate of the value of this socialisation is here. You and Darwin see it as a sort of accumulation which will end in an equilibrium. Can't you go further and admit that the 'pool' is not a *confluence* but a *convergence* of thought which given energy and 'drive' could give your 'Evolutionary Humanism' full value ? Another point. I fully agree that this game of chance involving its great numbers can propel a part of the universe towards the impossible, yet how do you explain this property of Natural Selection—that it persistently gives rise to unpredictable varieties more highly organised and consequently more consciously aware ? Can it be by accident that the *weltstoff* shows itself to be endowed with a certain attraction which like gravity makes us fall or rather rise, taking advantage of every chance, to the level of a greater

[1] Quoted by Teilhard from Boule, *Les Hommes fossiles,* and from J. Rostand, *Ce que je crois,* 1953.
[2] L.c. pp. 367–8.

complexity and a more sensitive consciousness ? If the *welt-stoff* is not basically 'loaded', how could it afford any opportunity for natural selection ?"

So he had written ; and the long paper *Les Singularités de l'homme* [1] that we are considering took up and developed the same questions. Teilhard is always sympathetic with his humanist friends, with Jean Rostand as years before with Vialleton, with Lucien Cuénot as with Marcellin Boule. He had injured his own reputation by urging his church to recognise the seriousness and the honesty of their criticisms and still quotes Édouard Le Roy in his script. [2] Here in this last exposition of his views his acceptance of their language and standpoint and his freedom from any sort of counter-attack or even debate are very notable—in striking contrast to the vilification and contempt which some of his English commentators have seen fit to employ against him.

Here he presents the purely physical aspect of the problem in terms more familiar to a British reader than those of his earlier writings, admits not without hesitation [3] an element of randomness operating among large numbers, [4] and stresses genetics and mutations, in a way hardly found in his earlier surveys. He also applies more definitely to the human level the philosophy and language of emergence which as we have seen is habitual for British but not for continental evolutionists. From his wide knowledge of mammalian palaeontology he draws attention to the fact that the appearance of new types seems to come rapidly at certain particular epochs. The forward movement is thus speeded up for example in the mid-tertiary era when primates, carnivores and ungulates appear almost simultaneously.

We may supplement this paper and modify its acceptance of randomness by reference to what is actually his last writing

---

[1] *L'Apparition*, pp. 295–369.   [2] L.c. p. 352.   [3] Cf. p. 306 note.
[4] He defines this as " capable of producing out of innumerable particles constantly in motion under pressure, during immense periods of time, the most improbable combinations ".

on the subject, *Une Défense de l'orthogenèse*, prepared for a conference to be held in April 1955 and published in *La Vision
du passé*, pp. 381–91. This in content and language shows
the influence upon him of his friend, Lucien Cuénot, whose
work he must have studied since his years in Paris with Boule
but whom he came to know intimately between 1947 and
1951. Cuénot had defined the principle of orthogenesis as
" seeming to predict a movement towards a result—such as
a new organ, a new structure, a new way of life " in his great
book *La Genèse des espèces animales*, third edition (Paris,
1932), p. 436, but had explained and illustrated it in great
detail on pp. 34–48 [1] and had stated that palaeontologists considered it as a continuous process affecting a mass of individuals
generation after generation, as they adjust themselves to a
changing environment. After examining many such cases he
concludes on p. 467 that there appears to be some factor either
in the structure of the germ-cells or exterior to them which
operates so as to initiate and control mutational sequences, and
that this would explain " coincidences "—and what some of
us call the problem of simultaneity, the appearance at the same
time of a number of different changes each essential to the
complete result. Teilhard, as several of his later papers testify,
accepted definitely but cautiously this principle and applied it
to human evolution. The difficulties which such acceptance
involved for him with his own Church, and indeed with many
other Christians, testify not only to the sincerity and strength
of his convictions but to his courage as a pioneer in proclaiming
them. The matter deserves illustration in some detail.

An example of the problem is admirably supplied by the
recent book *Evolution and Christians*, by Dr. T. G. Fothergill of
the Botanical Department of Durham University, published

[1] He mentions certain laws appropriate to it, notably that of irreversi-
bility (" what is lost cannot be recovered ") formulated by L. Dollo,
Teilhard's friend in 1924 when he was Director of the Royal Museum
of Natural History in Brussels. Teilhard quotes this in 1923, cf. *La Vision*,
p. 74.

with the *imprimatur* in 1961. Its author, a Catholic scholar and an ardent champion of evolution, has gathered a great mass of material to show the extent to which evolution as interpreted from Darwin onwards has been accepted and demonstrated in all the appropriate fields of scientific enquiry. His book is almost encyclopaedic in the range of its survey and the meticulous care with which technical terms are employed and explained, subjects of research are described and assessed, and the evidence set out objectively and estimated with sympathetic caution. It would surely be admitted that he has presented a case for the legitimacy of evolutionary ideas to his fellow-Catholics. But when this is granted it is unmistakably clear that in three vitally important respects his work is handicapped and defective. It is important that, with Teilhard in mind, these defects be considered.

In the first case Fothergill himself deplores the lack of any interpretation of science which sets modern knowledge in this field against a background of Christian or indeed any adequate philosophy. His own book reveals a complete lack of competent knowledge in this field. The names of all other English-speaking students in the time of Darwin and Huxley are omitted ; so are Bergson, Le Roy and Blondel, not to mention Lloyd Morgan, Whitehead and the rest. Reference to the Index of Prohibited Books goes some way to explain why in his inevitable references to the wider significance of evolution he can only name almost unknown and certainly nowhere representative thinkers. In consequence most of the significant consequences of belief in evolution, and almost all its influence upon the presentation of Christianity are ignored.

Secondly, the whole area that covers the evolution of behaviour patterns, the origin, fixation and effects upon mankind of instincts and habits, and the emergence of aesthetic, intellectual and ethical standards and ideals, is entirely ignored by him. He is concerned only with the physical aspect of the subject and with this at its pre-Christian, indeed pre-human level. The Catholic insistence that animals have no souls and the belief that each individual man receives a soul by a special divine act cuts away the deeper meaning of his work and reduces his theme to the level of a study of the mechanics of the process. This insistence upon the unique creation of mankind though not now necessarily an irreformable dogma is yet so general as to frustrate any profound interpretation of creation.

Thirdly, and this is perhaps the most serious difficulty, not only has any solution of the problems to be checked by its conformity with official doctrines, but every proposal must be submitted to and gain the assent of the Roman authorities, a body by no means necessarily expert who yet possess unlimited powers of veto. Definitions which are regarded as infallible and part of the Christian revelation are not only expressed in language and metaphors meaningless or mistaken for us to-day, but assume as facts myths and legends now hardly capable of modern acceptance and involving a cosmology and anthropology pre-Copernican and pre-Darwinian. We have only to note the efforts which Teilhard felt constrained to make in order to avoid a flat denial of the historicity of Adam and Eve to realise how the dead hand of the Pentateuch lies heavy upon honest attempts to proclaim a Christian doctrine of Creation to the modern world.

It is surely his ability and courage in dealing with these elements in the tradition which he inherited and loyally abstained from criticising that impress us with the quality of his mind and character. His continuous refusal to conceal or compromise his scientific convictions and his similar insistence that he cannot repudiate his vow of obedience or renounce his Church mark the nobility of his character. For he had, in fact, while growing up under these limitations, and indeed accepting them as imposing restrictions on his freedom of speech and publication, in his own thinking effectively transcended them. The first was overcome by his genius for friendship, for getting alongside men of all types and races and for working with entire candour and complete reciprocity with them. His familiarity with the thought of his time though basically that of French science, philosophy and religion, was as wide as his acquaintance with its representatives. We can trace how he grew not only into an increasing sensitiveness to the full range of modern knowledge, but into an understanding and use of its thought-forms and language. If, thanks to the Index, his early education lacked some of the scientific elements familiar to his British contemporaries, it gave him a broader and more integrated foundation onto which he built rapidly and continuously a wide and intimate superstructure of relevant knowledge.

Secondly, though geology not biology was his primary interest, and neither the "new psychology" nor the subsequent comparative psychology were his direct concern, it is obvious from his handling both of human problems and of the questions raised by Australopithecus and the whole research into man's origins that he had a keen interest in and acquaintance with the issues and a deep appreciation of their importance and possibilities. The trend of his mind from his earliest days was towards the futurity and wholeness of the world, and increasingly he saw the past only in relation to that which arose from and transformed it. The vistas opened up by studies in parapsychology and koenaesthesia,[1] though he could not speak with authority upon them, seemed important precisely because they drew attention to elements in evolution which foreshadowed new adventures and discoveries. The expansion of "conscience" and the passage from it to "reflexion" was always a subject of profound interest to him and especially in his later years he concentrated upon the study of it with a view to disclosing in what direction progress into the future was most likely.

Thirdly, we have seen that his African travels revealed his readiness to rethink and restate his own accepted conclusions.

[1] Cf. letter of Dr. M. Pobers in Cuénot, p. 377, on Teilhard's knowledge of modern psychology, of C. G. Jung, S. G. Soal and J. B. Rhine. Cf. also B. Towers, "Jung and Teilhard" in *The Wind and the Rain*, pp. 79–87.

It is significant that at this last stage of his life he became absorbed in the problems of the origin, development and significance of the continents—of the changes discoverable in their history and the effects of these upon the development of life upon them. He was not looking merely for the effects of its environment upon the origin and development of life —important as this obviously is—nor for the analogies between the growth of the great land masses and of the organisms evolving upon them, but as one who was convinced not only of the linkage between them, but of their complete interdependence and relationship. We who had tried to argue in our youth that the world was not the theatre on the stage of which man's drama of creation, fall and redemption was played out, but was itself an integral and essential part of the play, found him in his later years acting upon this conviction on a planetary scale. This insistence upon the wholeness of the cosmos had always been a cardinal point of his system : he held to it through all the tribulation that it involved for him : but nowhere did he apply it more largely than when he set out to investigate and trace the records and significance of the continents themselves. Geo-physics is the new science which he wished to see. He saw its emergence—and was glad.[1]

[1] Cf. *Letters from a Traveller*, pp. 355–8, letter of 12th December 1954.

CHAPTER SEVEN

TEILHARD AND EMERGENT EVOLUTION

ANYONE CLOSELY CONCERNED with the development of evolutionary and biological theories, especially if he belongs to the English-speaking world, will inevitably be confronted with the question what is the relation of Teilhard's thought to the British tradition of natural theology, and especially to the emphasis upon emergent evolution as expounded by Professor Conwy Lloyd Morgan in his Gifford Lectures [1] and subsequent books. It is obvious to any reader of the *Phenomenon* or any student of Teilhard's life that his scientific philosophy is closely parallel to it in scope, significance and even detail ; that his religious convictions in spite of differences of churchmanship are very similar ; and that his whole position might have been based upon the work being done in Britain at the very time when he was at Hastings. Yet by his French contemporaries, as by Sir Julian Huxley, he is treated as a lonely pioneer whose utterances are novel if not revolutionary and whose findings must be regarded as unprecedented ; and his first papers and lectures on evolution exposed him to condemnation and exile by his Church.

As we have seen, it is clear that until the last fifteen years of his life he had no close contact with British biologists or with the voluminous English literature on Darwinism ; that he was always a man of original and independent mind ; and that his language and mental equipment were those of French

[1] *Emergent Evolution*, 1923 ; *Life, Mind and Spirit*, 1926.

science and culture, and are still almost unintelligible to the Anglo-Saxon world. But even when full allowance is made for the different approach to nature between France and England and for the centuries-old cleavage over it between Britain and the continent, it is nevertheless manifest that Teilhard has a close, a very close, affinity to deep-rooted and native elements in that world's tradition.

The general attitude towards natural history was fifty years ago, and still is to a less extent, very characteristic of this difference. Even the most serious of the British " dailies " have never hesitated to record the arrival of swallows and the cuckoo, or the appearance of Camberwell Beauties or Lizard Orchids. Letters on such matters appear regularly in *The Times* : even to-day one does not see them in *Le Figaro*. Here bird-watchers can be numbered by the thousand ; so were moth-collectors fifty years ago. It is not that the French have not had since Buffon and Réaumur a long succession of naturalists and contributed books and research of outstanding value, but that, as the great brothers Jérôme and Jean Tharaud [1] have demonstrated, their attitude towards nature generally has been more detached, that during the period since A. Toussenel [2] and J. B. Bailly [3] there have been until Delamain no outstanding bird-books, and that it may easily be argued that Catholicism in its Latin form " shows only a very mediocre attention to animal-life ". It is unthinkable that in Britain so late as 1926 an exposition of Darwinism by so Christian a student as Teilhard or that in 1931 volumes as deeply religious as those of Édouard Le Roy could have been officially censured by Churchmen.

Moreover, if we go back to the seventeenth century and the days of Descartes it is plain that in Britain the Cartesian philosophy was principally and violently assailed not for its

---

[1] Cf. their letter to J. Delamain prefixed to his book *Why Birds sing*, pp. vii–xxi.

[2] Author of *Le Monde des oiseaux*.

[3] Cf. *Ornithologie de la Savoie*.

general principles but for its insistence that animals were mere automata. Mechanism was not unacceptable, but to the dog-lovers and field-naturalists and Platonists of Cambridge the defamation of sub-human life was an outrage. Henry More, whose mysticism led to a vivid belief in the Anima Mundi, and Ralph Cudworth with his clear and profound conception of the plasticity of nature united to condemn this aspect of Cartesianism ; and John Ray the naturalist set himself to collect evidence not only of canine intelligence and from the behaviour of chickens in his hen-run when a hawk flew over it or of moths in his breeding-cage where wild males " assembled " round a newly emerged female, but of the behaviour of a wide range of living organisms. Ray may indeed be regarded as the principal founder of the love of nature which gave to his fellow-countrymen the great succession of amateur zoologists, botanists and geologists to which William Paley, Gilbert White, Philip Gosse and, according to his latest biographer Loren Eiseley, Charles Darwin belonged and which was represented in Teilhard's time by a multitude in every field of science. It was this great company which welcomed the *Origin of Species* with such enthusiasm and realised as Charles Kingsley declared " that they have got rid of an interfering God—a master magician as I call it—and have to choose between the absolute empire of magic and a living, immanent, ever-working God ".[1] It is largely to this succession that British theology owes its peculiar quality, the insistence upon the worth of natural religion and upon what Ray called *The Wisdom of God in the works of Creation.*[2]

Ray had discussed the problems of form and function from the standpoint of the living organism, drawing evidence for belief in design from its reactions in behaviour as much as in structure. William Paley, a century later, in his *Natural Theology* had used much more mechanistic analogies : his idea of God was dominated by the pre-Christian concept of the

[1] *Life of C. K.*, II, p. 171.
[2] The title of his best known and most influential book.

divine engineer. In the nineteenth century from the Bridge-water Treaties to the strange mythology of Philip Gosse's *Omphalos* we can gauge the intensity of the struggle between the traditions of Genesis and the dawning knowledge of evolution. In such an atmosphere Darwin's work produced a sensation only comparable with that of Newton—and in its effect on religion far more revolutionary. Books like those of Henry Drummond and his followers in Scotland and the succession of Gifford lecturers strove to acknowledge and interpret the new outlook ; and, as T. H. Huxley admitted, the response of individual Christians was unexpectedly sympathetic. The love of nature asserted itself, and the extravagances of controversy were less violent than in Germany and America. But the conspiracy of silence which was designed to conceal the turmoil in England did not prevent its almost universal recognition.

In the first quarter of this century, whether we were working as biologists at the problem of the origin of life or as theologians at the doctrines of creation, Lloyd Morgan marked an epoch. A few philosophers might brush him aside as responsible only for a schema which clarified but did not explain, much as Teilhard by claiming to study only phenomena can be supposed not to deal with dogma or with metaphysics.[1] But as we learn to appreciate the true content of the thought of either of them, we know that in studying the appearance and shape of the evolutionary process they are inevitably dealing not only with the conditions that accompanied it and the pattern that it disclosed, but with its character, direction and significance, and therefore with the nature and reality of the universe itself. Certainly with both of them their interpretation of evolution disclosed elements and suggested qualities widely different from those commonly imagined, and in both

[1] For his relation to metaphysics cf. J. Daniélou, 'Signification de T. de C.', *Études*, Febr. 1962, pp. 145–62 ; and D. M. Mackinnon in *The Wind and the Rain* (ed. N. Braybrooke), London, 1962 ; and *The Modern Churchman*, vol. 5, pp. 195–9.

cases profoundly congruous with a religious and Christian outlook. Certainly to one who in his formative years had the guidance and friendship of Dr. Lloyd Morgan and followed up the final stages of his thought into his last writings, a first reading of the *Phenomenon of Man* made its general resemblance to the teaching of his predecessor immediately obvious. The language was different ; the line of approach showed little suggestion of direct contact ; the influence of Plato, so strong in England, was hardly perceptible ;[1] the sources except for general reference to Spinoza and their common acceptance of Darwin seemed quite independent, and yet the resulting exposition alike in its basic principles and in its general method was closely similar.

The interest thus aroused found no direct illumination from the full and impressive record of Teilhard's education, explorations and writings given by Dr. Cuénot. The casual contacts with England in Jersey and afterwards the years of study at the Jesuit centre at Ore, which certainly helped the integration of his life and thought, did not suggest any personal touch with Lloyd Morgan who only retired to Sussex after Teilhard's departure, or indeed with any English naturalists or thinkers directly associated with the study of Emergent Evolution. My concern remained dormant until in a letter to me Dr. Cuénot remarked " by the way you will have to reflect on the notion of emergence " : then interest exploded into excitement. To explain this explosion a reminiscence may be permissible.

It was in 1926 that in the course of my duties at the Cathedral in Liverpool and in connection with my first book on the subject, I put on a course of lectures on Science and Religion dealing largely with Evolution. My orthodox Darwinian upbringing had been heavily influenced by work with William Bateson and study of the Mendel-De Vries alternative

[1] In his war-time letters he admits to having no first-hand knowledge of Plato (*Genèse*, p. 292) though he quotes θεὸς ἀεὶ γεωμετρεῖ in Greek (p. 315).

to Darwinism : but though wholly convinced that evolution was firmly established and far more revolutionary in its effects than Christians had recognised, I was still uncommitted to any particular theory. The lectures as planned attempted to describe the facts which presented creation to us not as an event " in the beginning " but as a continuous process, and so to deal with the struggle for existence and its effects, and then with mutations and their evident importance. At that point I had no clear conclusion. But I was reading *Life, Mind and Spirit*, the second and more exciting volume of Lloyd Morgan's Giffords. No book till Teilhard has thrilled me so much. Here was a coherent assembling of the data which did not assume a contrast between physical and mental or soul and body. Here was a system continuous and consistent, which allowed for what one of my teachers, A. S. Pringle-Pattison, had called " the twin aspects of the cosmic history, continuity of process and the emergence of real differences ".[1] I made time to read and digest the Giffords between my own lectures and to finish up with a summary of their vindication of Christian theology—though I never discovered how many of my audience realised that during the course a basic change in my own outlook had taken place ! My Hulsean lectures in Cambridge, Noble lectures in Harvard, and book *The Creator Spirit* were the first results of this change. No wonder that for me Dr. Cuénot had struck a note that echoed across the years.

Going back a generation it is plain how fully in all the principal points of his cosmology Lloyd Morgan agrees with Teilhard. For me he was among the first to shake the traditional dualism of my outlook. Body and soul, the piano and its player—how strongly in the days of aggressive materialism that contrast had impressed itself—even though the technique which produced music by the action of one upon the other was hard to explain. Was there a connection ? Plato had never quite convinced us of it ; Professor Ryle had not yet

[1] *The Idea of God*, p. 103.

ridiculed the " ghost in the machine ". Lloyd Morgan had not (I think) fully reached the psychosomatic outlook which advances in medicine and more grudgingly in physiology have established for us ; and he did not accept as plainly as one or two of his contemporaries have done an avowed panpsychism. But he insisted repeatedly that every event in our experience could be described both in physical and in psychological terms ; and that the two tales of its processes were as he called them " concomitant ".[1] He gave us a picture of the " thing in itself" whether cell or saint as being describable in the two categories, these two not being confused, and of the causality of events, depending not upon one or upon the other, but upon the entity itself, its whole nature and circumstances. Further, he taught us that the elements themselves from atom to man were so constituted that under appropriate conditions and in the proper relationship they could occasion the emergence of the novel and unpredictable. The pattern of their relatedness whether of atoms in the molecule, or of cells in the organism, or of ideas in the mind might give rise to the emergence of a new level of being. This pattern he did not hesitate to describe as a fellowship [2]—a less immediately colourless word than complexification and convergence, but suggestive of analogies in terms of the personal rather than the abstract, and as such making it easier for him to point to love rather than power or wisdom as being the source and quality of creativity. He had only to add that from this position he could readily accept and proclaim the appropriateness of the emergence in Christ of the unique and divine to make his similarity to Teilhard obvious.

Lloyd Morgan was an elderly man when he produced his lectures and even then his style did not make for easy reading

---

[1] Cf. *Life, Mind and Spirit*, pp. 1–30, etc.
[2] Cf. *Mind at the Crossways*, p. 6, etc. Here is a strong link with what Teilhard meant by his latest neologism, " amorisation ", and with his famous saying " The social must not be separated from the cellular " (cf. *Le Figaro*, 5th February 1962).

or, always, for clear perception of the fullness of his thought ;
and in his subsequent books [1] the discussion was often obscure
and the language occasionally mannered. But like Teilhard
he had a very wide range of knowledge and of interests. A
personal pupil of Thomas Henry Huxley, a zoologist, morpho-
logist and taxonomist, he developed a keen interest in and
profound knowledge of behaviour-problems and comparative
psychology. He was in fact the pioneer of the sort of studies
by which his friend and pupil H. Eliot Howard developed
theories of bird territory and song and of the " bird mind ".
His methods of objective and sensitive observation disclosed
to us the absurdities of our popular natural history and the
importance and difficulties of meticulous accuracy. To him
more than to any others, except W. H. Hudson and E. C.
Selous, the widespread passion for bird-watching owes its
origin. In addition as a lifelong teacher and finally as Vice-
Chancellor of a great University he had abundant human
sympathies and contacts, and a strong religious life. Personally
modest, generous and averse from controversy, he was in
those days almost alone in his insistence that the current
mechanism was wholly inadequate. In consequence he has
never received the tribute that he deserved—though he will
now surely attract attention as among the most important of
the group who prepared the way for the widespread response
to Teilhard. To those who had long been waiting for an
interpretation of evolution as a continuous and universal
process displaying a congruity of method and a step-by-step
development towards a richer and more complex organisation
his scheme was an invaluable contribution.

It was given a specifically theological application when
Dr. L. S. Thornton of Mirfield employed it in his Christo-
logical treatise *The Incarnate Lord*. Outlining in some fullness
the successive levels of emergence manifested in creation he
treated the coming of Jesus Christ as the crown of the whole
adventure and proclaimed him, or so it seemed, as the fully

[1] *The Animal Mind*, 1930 ; *The Emergence of Novelty*, 1933.

emergent deity. At first sight it appeared that at last we had a theology which treated Creation, Redemption and Sanctification as one process, and evolution as progressing towards and consummated in the cosmic Christ. Unfortunately when more closely examined it appeared that the author could not bring himself to admit that the Incarnate was in fact within the series, and the whole a *scala divinitatis*. Tradition was too strong ; God must be the " wholly other " and the Saviour an intruder from another world. So at the close it was insisted that Christ represented not the final summation but a unique act of God discontinuous with, because radically different from, all that had gone before. We were left with the conclusion that for Dr. Thornton the pageant of the cosmic process made no essential contribution to the Advent which had seemed to be its climax. His Christology was no longer Pauline but Apollinarian if not docetic.[1]

Nevertheless even if theological orthodoxy was not yet ready to receive the consequences of a full acceptance of evolution, the fact remained that a scientist of high standing had given an interpretation of it free from the radical dualism and inconsistencies of the past and presenting us with the picture of one universal, orderly and coinherent divine activity, moving upward and onward with an ever-expanding complexity alike of structure and of consciousness, and having man as its culmination and Christ as its consummation. The solution was still at all levels of its progress relatively incomplete. From cosmic origins and interplanetary communication and from nuclear energy and molecular analysis on to the electron-microscope, the investigation of extrasensory perception and psychosomatic medicine, there has been growth of knowledge both rapid and various. But it is still fair to say that the main lines of Teilhard's thought had been sketched out, and a new outlook broadly established.

For at least in the English-speaking world Lloyd Morgan was not alone. Samuel Alexander, the philosopher of Man-

[1] Cf. *The Incarnate Lord*, pp. 232–9.

chester University, had published his Gifford Lectures, *Space, Time and Deity*, A. N. Whitehead had followed up his brilliant career as a mathematician in Cambridge as the partner of Bertrand Russell in *Principia Mathematica* by a professorship in philosophy at Harvard and the series of books beginning with *The Concept of Nature* in 1920 and *Science in the Modern World* in which he developed an evolutionary system on the lines of a modern and highly original Platonism. Though his language was often difficult and he worked out his own position with a great knowledge of the philosophy of the eighteenth century but without much indebtedness to contemporary thinkers his two later books *Religion in the Making* and *Process and Reality* contributed much to the point of view which we have been considering. So, too, Field-Marshal Smuts had expounded his interpretation of life in terms of what Teilhard called complexification and convergence in the remarkable book *Holism and Evolution*—a book of which his own personal and political life was a striking example and whose message Teilhard sums up in the single underlined sentence, "Everything forms a single whole" (*Milieu*, p. 33).[1] These and others like Gerald Heard whose *Ascent of Man* Teilhard read in 1944 represented the movement of thought to which he is so remarkably akin.

There is, nevertheless, so far as can be discovered, no evidence that at any time in his life he had any direct contact or close linkage with Lloyd Morgan or any of the British tradition that we have been considering. He was, as we have noted, not a great reader or much dependent upon a wide bibliographical knowledge : the card-index and the collection of cross-references were not essential instruments of his work : and hence came his independence, coherence and consistency.

---

[1] It is a book in which the principle of emergence is fully developed until the last chapter. In this the Dutch Calvinist fundamentalism of his youth compelled him to reject the theistic and Christian conclusion which his argument demanded and which he promised before his death to provide in a revised edition.

But in his *Phenomenon* there is one footnote which reveals an immediate contact with a clear though brief exposition of "the doctrine of emergence". This is to be found on p. 57 in which Teilhard states that some time after his sections on "the within" had been written he had found "their substance in some masterly lines written by J. B. S. Haldane", the outstanding British biologist. He then quotes two sentences from the address on "Science and Ethics" in Haldane's book of collected essays, *The Inequality of Man*, on p. 113. The book was published in London in 1932 and the particular lecture was delivered in 1928. Haldane gives in a few brilliantly lucid paragraphs an exposition of emergence exactly similar to the process of complexification, convergence and consummation which Teilhard's book has expounded. Later in it (*Phenomenon*, p. 269) [1] he calls his own exposition "the Principle of Emergence" and refers again to J. B. S. Haldane whom in fact he met in Paris at the International Conference of Palaeontology in April 1947. [2] But by that time he had been in close touch with Sir Julian Huxley, and had become familiar with the British point of view ; and this had influenced his vocabulary and to some small extent his method of presenting his philosophy.

In his earlier work he seldom uses the word emergence [3] and then usually—as in relation to the analogy of the Baptism of Christ (*Milieu*, p. 94)—in a general sense. In the *Phenomenon* the more technical meaning appears in an important passage (p. 79) where he writes of "the emergence of the microscopic from the molecular, of the organic from the chemical, of the living from the pre-living" and adds "a metamorphosis of this sort could not be the result of a simple

---

[1] In the French edition the two references to Haldane are on pp. 53-4 and p. 299.   [2] Cf. Cuénot, p. 336.

[3] Dr. Cuénot tells me that Teilhard used two words, "immersion" to denote the coming together of the elements, "emergence" to define the result of their union.

continuous process". Similarly in his illustrative material there is no direct reference to Lloyd Morgan's most familiar example, the concurrence of hydrogen and oxygen in due proportion occasioning the emergence of a new and unpredictable element, water. But to illustrate the emergence of reflection at the point at which anthropoids gave rise to man he uses a very similar example drawn from the sudden eruption of steam when water is heated to boiling point.[1] His emphasis is generally upon the gradualness, not the immediacy, of the coming of novelty ; and this is probably due to a marked characteristic, or, as some would regard it, a definite defect in his position. For, as we have noted, his general approach to the origin of species is nowhere strongly influenced by genetics or the facts of mutation, and this may account for his stress upon the long preparation needed for change and upon what he calls the " disappearance of the pedicels "—the fact that processes which lead to the evolution of new types though they are generally very slow leave almost no record, and that thus their results give a spurious effect of suddenness. But at least the whole impact of Mendelism upon biology in Britain and America, which led to a strong belief in the importance of real novelty in cosmic as in organic progress, hardly affected Teilhard's thinking until late in his life.[2] The matter is not, I think, of any great importance in estimating his achievement : but it demonstrates the extent to which he was untouched by men who in general so closely approximate to him. The loss is, of course, largely due to his exile in China and his constant travelling.

But in fairness to him it must be admitted that even in the English-speaking world the movement, of which Lloyd Morgan was from the scientific side the most constructive

---

[1] *Phenomenon*, p. 168.

[2] In 1937 when he received the Mendel medal at Villanova College, U.S.A., he spoke briefly of Mendel in stressing the importance of combining biological research and experimentation with the palaeontological approach to the problems of human evolution.

representative, was overwhelmed before it had the opportunity to establish itself securely. Events in the economic and political sphere, typified by the financial crisis in America in 1930 and the long years of unemployment in Britain, and by the rise of Fascism and Nazism, synchronised with and were reflected by the revolt of Protestant theology against liberal and rationalistic attempts to interpret the faith in terms of the cosmology, anthropology and psychology of the modern world, against critical exegesis of biblical and dogmatic traditions, and against the social and collective movement in human relationships. We must never be blind to the heroic resistance of Dr. Karl Barth to the subservience of the " German Christians " to Hitler, his insistence that the State must obey God rather than its Führer, his leadership of the Confessional Church, and more recently his protests against German rearmament. Nevertheless his exaggerated transcendentalism, his denunciation of the worth of human effort, and his perverse exegesis of St. Paul gave his followers in Britain and America a message of pessimism, helplessness and despair which swept over the popular religion of the churches and seminaries of the reformed denominations. Fundamentalism, which had seemed to meet its deathblow at the Dayton trial in Tennessee, was revived as Biblical Theology, and its combination of individualism and authoritarianism proved irresistibly attractive. The " great blight ", as it may now be called,[1] ignored and so reopened the old conflicts between science and religion, went near to replacing " the Jesus of history " by the Christ of a new Mithraism, and under the title of neo-orthodoxy asserted the terrestrial supremacy of sin and repudiated belief in earthly progress, or human effort, or the hope of a universal Christendom. The Oecumenical Movement which had started so valiantly in the twenties changed and narrowed its presentation of the Gospel and the methods of its evangelism ; and the Calvinism of the Swiss and Dutch churches powerfully influenced Scotland, had many prominent spokesmen in the

[1] Cf. above, Chapter One, pp. 24–9.

United States, and made work along the line of reinterpretation very difficult.

Roman Catholicism was saved from this reaction by the strength and vitality of its Thomist inheritance.[1] Though Existentialism owed its origin to the disillusionment and pessimism of the time, and in its quality had some affinity with Protestant neo-orthodoxy, it did not infect the wisdom or challenge the tradition established by the great Schoolmen of the thirteenth century, and in the last thirty years restated by a number of scholars. The best known of them, Étienne Gilson [2] and Jacques Maritain, held the field all over the world and indeed initiated important attempts to apply the principles of St. Thomas to the modern problems raised by science and sociology. Though the doctrinal innovation and official policy of the Vatican made it evident that no concession to liberalism could be expected, at least an enlightened Scholasticism saved most churchmen from the sort of frustration which the contrast between the immensity of our opportunity and the inadequacy of our equipment made almost inevitable. If under the circumstances Rome could not at once endorse or authorise Teilhard's message, at least it did not condemn him —except to silence. It waited on the event, without (it appears) any recognition of its importance!

And for us who cannot accept the method or many of the detailed findings of Scholasticism it is a cause of thankfulness that in the manifold inheritance of Christendom is so strong a tradition on behalf of the necessity of a reasonable faith. To it we largely owe the speed with which an anti-rational and pessimistic presentation of the Gospel has broken down, and the readiness of Christians everywhere to respond to Teilhard's message.

But those who have held fast to the concept of emergent evolution during the difficult years of reaction and pessimism,

[1] For the relation between Teilhard and St. Thomas cf. Étienne Borne (Cuénot, pp. 293, 479).

[2] Whom Teilhard met in 1954 (Cuénot, p. 438).

when Teilhard himself was forbidden to publish his views or give us his encouragement, will perhaps feel that by this very prohibition his vision has now secured a welcome which it could not have received in the thirties and forties. Only let us not forget those who saw and stated the same conviction, and in our desire to exalt its new prophet cut him off from the colleagues who did so much to prepare his way.

And for Teilhard himself the connection is made obvious and specific in his latest writings. Take, for example, the short paper that he wrote upon "Hominisation et spéciation" in mankind which was in the *Revue Scientifique* for November 1952 and is included in the third printed volume of his collected works *La Vision du passé*. Here, after briefly describing the evolution of species throughout the realm of organic life, he claims that in one sense man is a species like any other but yet different from them. Man represents a species which has jumped forward biologically : "réfléchi", self-consciousness, has emerged in him ; and in consequence his specific distinctiveness enables work on a new and cultured level, and tends to lift him from the condition of an aggregate, or mass of units, to that of a centralised and co-operative unity. For mankind emergence effects not a mere difference of degree as between the anthropoid and the human, but a real novelty. Evolution remains the same : it continues but has in man passed a critical point which changes the biological level to that of culture, *Différentiation culturelle* now equals *spéciation hominisée*. This human development does not necessarily exclude the recurrence of genetic mutations ; the cultural level does not appear to modify the genes : but our special inheritance is not now a matter of chromosome but of education.

On the strictly scientific side of thought about evolution the story is somewhat similar to that which we have traced in the religious record of the revolt against the theory of emergence. In the twenties it had seemed that the old antitheses, Lamarck or Darwin, natural selection or genetic mutation, physical change or responsive behaviour were being resolved. Biology, which twenty years before had almost forfeited its right to its name since it was concerned not with life but with dead organisms in laboratories or museums, was passing through its phase of " cages and mazes " and was beginning to follow medicine into the recognition of the vital significance of environment and relationships. But it too suffered a reaction. Though behaviourism never seriously infected Britain, neo-Darwinianism rebelled against the evidence that natural selection was not the sole factor in evolutionary progress and refused to acknowledge or discuss the fatal objections which challenge its monopoly. There was, and still to some extent is, a reaction to an exclusive and militant orthodoxy, limited, as Teilhard noted, to the Anglo-Saxon world, and even there speedily losing its authority—but very vocal!

It is impossible here to do more than mention a few typical cases which have compelled biologists to recognise that in evolution, at least from the beginnings of organic life, the behaviour of the individual towards its neighbours and its environment is a factor of increasing importance as life expands its range of activities. The correlation of structural changes between male and female as Lucien Cuénot reported in certain crabs, the necessarily simultaneous achievement of their complicated sexual and copulatory habits among dragon-flies, the four or five separate events involving simultaneous changes which accomplish the parasitism of the cuckoo, failure in any one of which would have lethal consequences, such are examples of the relationship of the creature to its world. So are the simpler problems of the effect of habits and discoveries upon the life-pattern and the speed with which these become universal to the species, as in the part played by education in the development of bird-song or (to be concrete) the universal puncturing of milk-bottle lids by tits. In face of such multiform evidence as of all recent study of the capabilities of animate nature it is ridiculous to limit our estimate of evolution to the purely physical chemical elements in it or to treat them in strict segregation from what Professor Waddington calls the continuum.

All this indicates how right zoologists are to assert the place of human self-consciousness in determining the future. But if good evolutionists, they must realise that this involves an abandonment of their mechanisms—unless of course they come to believe in sudden miracles and forswear the *Descent of Man*. Sir Julian and the neo-Darwinians cannot have it both ways. If the world is a cosmos and evolution its history, then progress must be judged not only by its origins but by its results. No honest student of it can ignore the fact that this planet has been the birthplace of life and man, of Christ and the saints.

CHAPTER EIGHT

TEILHARD AND ST. PAUL

AMONG ALL THE HESITATION and debates about the orthodoxy or otherwise of the Teilhardian religious philosophy, and
when it is suggested that its author if not a pantheist is at least
tainted with Origenism or that if a Catholic is surely not a
traditionalist, one plain fact needs to be generally recognised.
It is, of course, emphasised by Tresmontant[1] and Rabut,
though without a very adequate appreciation of its character.
Teilhard in his whole Christian vision of the process of Cosmogenesis and Christification is actually and avowedly restating
for us the theology of St. Paul as this came to its fullest expression. Dr. Cuénot, though he does not give it special
treatment or account for its place in Teilhard's life, quotes
constant evidence that St. Paul is the principal source and guide
of his thought and speech. But we need not go further than
Le Milieu divin for proof. Its first section is concerned to
affirm the Pauline exhortation : " Whatever you do, do it in
the name of our Lord Jesus Christ " and to expand it so that
all our deeds and thoughts, all our being, may be literally " in
Christ ". Those two words, as Adolf Deissmann taught us,
are fundamental to the Apostle's message as they are to
Teilhard's version of it. When he opens the final part of his
book by quoting " Whether we live or die we are Christ's "
and adds " the first two parts of this essay are simply an analysis
and verification of the above words of St. Paul ," he confirms
this truth. It is the unity of all life in Christ that gives its

[1] He has published a small book on St. Paul (Paris, 1956).

coherence to his outlook ; and as his knowledge of cosmology, biology and anthropology spread and deepened, it merely expanded his sense of the universalism, personalism and consummation that is guaranteed by a full understanding of the cosmic Christ as St. Paul came to declare it in his three last great epistles Philippians, Colossians and Ephesians. And the process of Pauline interpretation in this early book of Teilhard could be traced right through his writings until the fully developed and emphasised Christ-mysticism of his last utterances.

Before we examine this matter in detail there are three points which must be noted.[1] They help to explain why to so many Christians Teilhard's work seems strange and dubiously orthodox.

In the first place the famous dictum of Professor Harnack, " In the second generation of Christians only one man, Marcion, understood St. Paul—and he misunderstood him " [2] cannot be seriously challenged. From the time of Clement of Rome onwards St. Paul was freely quoted and generally reverenced, but the quotations hardly ever touch the depths or even the religion of his writings. They are concerned with his utterances against the Law and the Jews, his rulings upon Church behaviour and morals, his advice of obedience to the secular authorities, and his warnings against lapses into factions or paganism. Though he had rejected legalism and institutionalism and spent his life striving to replace them by a new kind of free and organic community, he was used if at all to build up a disciplined and obedient and conventional society. On the great dogmatic, hierarchical, liturgical and ethical issues with which Church leaders were mainly concerned he was with difficulty employed ; of the inwardness, the grace and love, the full-knowledge and fellowship, of his message, there

[1] For fuller treatment of these points and of the development of St. Paul's thought see my recent book, *St. Paul and the Gospel of Jesus* (London, 1961).

[2] In *Ency. Brit.*, 11th ed., XVII, p. 692.

was little sign of awareness in the life and thought of Christendom. Clement and Origen of Alexandria among the Greeks
appreciated the universalism of his mysticism, and Augustine
among the Latins glimpsed the agonies and ecstasies of his
soul : but most of the Greeks were absorbed with intellectual
argument, and most of the Latins with efficient organisation,
and the experience of life in Christ was for them both shared
mainly by participation in worship and sacraments—that is
in specifically religious activities. It only needed the doctrine
of the two swords, and the double standard of clergy and
laity, to divide the one world into two, the sacred and the
profane.

Secondly, it is also true that from the days of the writing
of the Second Epistle of St. Peter it has been stated and believed
that in St. Paul's letters are " things hard to understand which
ignorant and ill-balanced men twist to their own destruction "
(iii. 16). And this understates the position. There are two
main reasons for the general belief that St. Paul's letters if not
self-contradictory are so involved and allusive that only the
learned specialist can make much of their meaning. First, of
course, the Athenians were not wholly libellous when they
called him a " seed-picker ",[1] one who was ready to fasten on
any rag of argument or idea and swallow it. As we can see,
he did in fact snatch any sort of imagery from the race-track
or the wrestling-school, the pagan poets or the rabbinic class-
room, the market-place or the synagogue and use it to illustrate a point or enforce a conclusion. Add to that his frequently
involved or disjointed sentences—due partly to the speed of
his mind and partly perhaps to the shortcomings of his secretary
—and you realise how difficult it can be for men of a different
age and temper to follow the flow of his meaning. Again,
he suffers more than any other biblical writer from the belief
in verbal inspiration or from the equally damaging conviction
that all his writings are not only inspired but wholly consistent
and of identical authority. It is only if we recognise that his

[1] Acts xvii. 18.

letters are genuine messages sent at different periods of his own growth to folks of different race, place, circumstances and needs, and that they form a series each representing not only a particular intention but in almost every case a new stage in his insight and interpretation, that we can grasp the sequence and fulfilment of his gospel. It is surely obvious that the strong but limited concept of Christ in Galatians is distinct from the crude eschatology of Thessalonians, or the fresh insight and explorations at Corinth, the philosophy of history in Romans, or the Christ-centred universalism of the last three certainly authentic writings—the three to which Teilhard is principally indebted.

Thirdly, a word must be said about those who maintain that St. Paul's cosmic interpretation has little valid connection with Jesus in his historic life and ministry. Nowadays indeed the familiar idea that the Apostle took the name and martyrdom of Jesus of Nazareth and adopted it as the myth of a Christic mystery-religion has been largely abandoned—since the evidence of St. Paul's acquaintance with mystery-religions is very small and so far as it goes opposed to such a theory ; and his relationship both with Jesus and with the Apostolic Church is now more generally recognised. But it remains true that the picture of Jesus in the Synoptic Gospels looks at first sight very different from that suggested by the Christ-mysticism of the Apostle. It is only when we appreciate the extent to which St. Paul is simply following the general movement of all the early disciples—trying to find an adequate answer to the question, What think ye of Christ ? or to put it more simply, trying to explain the impact which Jesus had made upon him and his world—that we can see his own progress in its true setting and proportion. Of course all the writings concerning Jesus reflect the impression of his words and works since his first public appearance in the synagogue at Capernaum when men murmured " What is this ? A new sort of teaching. With authority ! " (Mark i. 27). We can trace through St. Mark's Gospel the crescendo of their appraisal of him—to St. Peter's confession " Thou art the Christ " and to the Centurion's at the Cross. St. Paul, as we shall see, took up the task when having been disappointed by the failure of Jesus to escape the accursed death he had his consequent repudiation challenged on the Damascus road. Thenceforward we can follow the stages of his developing experience of the divine status and universal significance of the Christ.

As will be seen when we come to examine the final phases of their thought, the resemblance between Teilhard and the Apostle is obvious and indisputable. The vision of the cosmic Christ presented in the three last epistles is translated by Teilhard into the language and imagery and set against the background of a " cosmogenesis " acceptable to twentieth-century science. But their identical conclusions derive from starting-points and express temperaments and experiences that at first sight differ widely ; and this accounts for the freely repeated criticism that whereas St. Paul preaches Christ cruci-fied, Teilhard concentrates not upon Calvary but upon Easter and Pentecost. As this is an evident objection both to his Paulinism and in some quarters to his theology it is a point of some importance.

Saul of Tarsus according to the evidence both of the Acts and of his own statements had been brought up a Pharisee, one of those whose loyalty to the Law and to the Messianic hope gave them both an interest in the prophet of Nazareth and a dilemma over his attitude to the Sabbath, the Tradition and indeed the whole ceremonial and moral system of Judaism. As a pupil of Gamaliel and one who had known Jesus " after the flesh "[1] he must have belonged to the large section of Jewish opinion which though it did not take part in his arrest yet welcomed its issue as a plain test. The sentence of cruci-fixion involved the death " upon a tree " specially cursed by the Law (Deut. xxi. 23) : if Jesus succumbed to it, God's verdict against him was clear : if he was Messiah, then he

---

[1] Cf. 2 Cor. v. 16 : whether this implies physical contact is disputed, and for our present purpose not important.

would come down from the Cross ; God or Elijah would rescue him. Saul accepted the ordeal, and its result ; and his persecuting zeal is proof of the bitterness of his resentment. Hence the violence and power of his conversion-experience which signalised him as typically " twice-born " ; and proved to him that the death of Jesus had been divinely overruled, that the Law was thereby disowned by God, and that with it the whole of Pharisaic Judaism was overthrown. The Cross was now for Saul the symbol of redemption from legal servitude (Gal. iii. 13), the initiation into the new life, the decisive event in God's dealings with Israel.

The distinction between the once- and twice-born is neither universal nor, except in extreme cases, profound : but plainly Teilhard's upbringing and character disallowed any such revolution. He grew up in a devotedly Christian family and with a fully Catholic acceptance of creed and church and cultus. He came to Christ not from the historic ministry and its dramatic close but from experience of the Eucharist and of the Sacred Heart in the imagery of which his earlier presentations *Le Christ dans la matière* (1916) and *La Messe sur le monde* (1923) are fashioned. As he grows into a larger and more varied life and faces the problems of intellectual readjustment and of a world-wide mission, he has to deal with the sort of questions which confronted St. Paul—the relation of Christ to men of alien culture and ethics, of sceptical and humanistic philosophies, of social, economic and political ideals vastly different from those of his own world, and of a community not of organisation but of the Spirit. In so doing he moved along a road increasingly close to that of St. Paul and with an increasing identity of conviction. Moreover, though his youthful dedication left no room for a conversion he did experience under the influence of his first contact with Bergson's *Creative Evolution* a revolutionary change in his cosmic philosophy. He had up till then accepted the traditional view of the fixity of species and apparently not realised the importance of Darwinism except as an interesting hypothesis. Bergson made him not only a convinced evolutionist but one who was not content with the *élan vital* or life-force operating upon and striving to mould obdurate and pre-existing matter. He quickly reformed his concepts so as to insist that the process was not only formative and continuous but universal : evolution became for him synonymous with our whole concept of the cosmos. More and more fully he realised that all things are in Christ, moving onwards and upwards in him. His years in the war tested the whole scope and character of his upbringing and confronted him with the problem of the Gentile world.[1] " We Christians must learn to humanise our saintliness." [2]

A vivid light is thrown upon the quality and scope of his thought if we study and summarise the stages by which St. Paul starting with his conversion-experience was led to challenge and reshape all his ideas of God, the world and mankind, and to reach the Cosmic Christ from whom and through whom and in whom, as. he came to affirm, all things consist and the divine *pleroma* dwells ; the Christ by whom Teilhard's thought is dominated and whom he proclaims in wholly Pauline language.

For Saul of Tarsus, Hebrew of the Hebrews, Jew of the Dispersion, Roman citizen, pupil of Gamaliel, conversion had meant not only release from a discipline legal, institutional and racial, which had been the complete frame-work of his training and prospects, but initiation into a new and personal relationship and an unexplored world without landmarks but eminently suited to his alert and adventurous character. He had the intelligence to grasp the revolutionary scale of the event, the imagination to attempt readjustment of his whole outlook and career, and the courage to face the loneliness and hardships involved. Those who have named him " Paul the dauntless " and " the dreamer whose dreams came true " have indicated the magnitude of his adventure. Fortunately, like Teilhard, he had no domestic or financial ties : he was wise

[1] Cf. above, Chapter Four, pp. 75–9.   [2] *Genèse*, p. 288.

165

enough to take time, in Arabia (Gal. i. 17), to prepare himself for his new life : and he came back with a sufficient sense of the quality and effects of his experience to be able to put it into action.

If the death of Christ and God's vindication of him had demonstrated the failure of the Law, then access to God in Christ could not be made conditional upon the fulfilment of legal obligations : a new way to God had been opened, and the fenced road of circumcision and the Mosaic Code was no longer compulsory. No doubt his adventures in Antioch and Tarsus before his first missionary journey clinched his conviction that the Gospel was universal in its claim. How strongly he felt this is made plain by the passion and violence of his first letter dealing with the challenge to his work in Galatia and written shortly after his return from Derbe, Lystra and Iconium. The free admission of Gentiles to the Church was plainly the crucial issue on which his whole concept of life in Christ then depended. It was not, as the pioneers of higher criticism supposed, a primary and continuing conflict : whatever the exact sequence of events underlying the Epistle to the Galatians and the relevant chapters in the Acts, the issue was decided by Apostolic verdict, and decided without leaving much trace of bitterness. But while it lasted, the struggle was acute ; and the Epistle shows not only how strongly St. Paul felt and suffered during it, but how remarkably in the midst of its controversy and argumentation his own truer insight is revealed in the three flashes of illumination which break through the complaints and sophistries of its chief contents. " I have been crucified with Christ : yet I am alive : not I ; but Christ lives in me " (ii. 19, 20). " There is neither Jew nor Greek, bond nor free, male nor female : ye are all one person in Christ Jesus " (iii. 18) and " The fruit of the Spirit is love and joy, peace and fortitude, mercy and virtue, faith which is self-committal, humility which is self-emptying, temperance which is God-control " (v. 22-3)—these three sayings foreshadow his mature message, the fullness of life in Christ and its universality which includes and integrates all the best in human activity and ethics.

But there was still a long way to go. His entry into Europe, standing on his dignity at Philippi, preaching crude Eschatology, the coming of Jesus as king soon and in splendour, at Thessalonica, and the admirable but unconvincing lecture on the Unknown God at Athens, displays the extent to which he had become all things to all men (1 Cor. ix. 22) and so doing had huckstered the Gospel. He went to Corinth humbled by failure ; and then in his humiliation discovered that it was useless to accommodate his message to traditional ideas or the prejudices of his audience, that Christ could not be loosely attached to non-Christian or pre-Christian philosophies or ideas of God, that if Jesus was like God then God must be like Jesus, and that therefore neither the God of Battles nor the Designer and Engineer, neither power nor wisdom was the ultimate attribute of deity. In Christ crucified God is revealed as the only true power and wisdom ; and the definition of Godhead as love and fatherhood is affirmed. And with this as his new criterion he can answer the speculative and ethical problems of his converts and rise from the concept of the Christian community as an organised society to that of an incorporate organism, the " body " of God, having many members differing in function but equal in status, and integrated by love.

So he can proceed to the philosophy of history, the interpretation of nature human and divine, in our Epistle to the Romans—that all creation reveals God, and that men can be transformed by committal to God in Christ, that the aspiration and travail of nature is not apart from but pervaded and enabled by the Spirit of God, and that through its failures it nevertheless moves forward towards fulfilment, since in fact "all things co-operate for good to men who love God" (Rom. viii. 28). Against so clearly formulated a background he can work out the full significance of the Gospel. Jesus in his ministry gave us the revelation of it ; as we share his mind and abandon our pride and self-reliance we shall discover how to live joyously, and shall find all the world already permeated by the divine "values", truth, goodness, purity, loveliness, excellence (Phil. ii. 5–11 and iv. 8). And the scope of this life in Christ is not a limited or private possession. Christ is himself the complete reflection of the divine, the "pleroma" or totality of Godhead, embracing in himself all the qualities of mature and perfect life. We can each and all become completely conscious of his manifold and universal presence and united by it in the community that incorporates his Spirit. This "full knowledge" becomes for us an immediate and spontaneous substitute for law so that "in Christ" we both know what we ought to do and also have laid on us the constraint and power to do it (Col. ii. 1–7).

Hence in his final treatise, the so-called Epistle to the Ephesians, he can give us the full vision of Christ as the "Consummator" of all things, in whom the whole universe finds its integration and fulfilment and "we all come home unto the unity of our faith and our full knowledge of the Son of God, unto mature manhood, even the measure of the stature of the totality of Christ" (Eph. iv. 13). Here is the vision of unity in diversity, universality enriched by but including all particularities, an all-embracing personality, the Christ that is to be. This is the vision which now for a century, and for us in Britain ever since Frederic Denison Maurice,[1] has inspired the pioneers of social welfare and the prophets of international co-operation. That it is all-inclusive in the sense that its membership transcends all ecclesiastical as well as racial, social and sexual barriers, may not be confidently affirmed—though the Apostle is in these last letters almost silent upon "religious" rites, practices and obligations. But for the student of Teilhard there is manifestly complexity and convergence, unanimisation and Christification.

This brief sketch, different as it may appear from the ideas

[1] Presiding in 1854 over the first Co-operative Conference, Maurice defined the basic principles of Co-operation in terms of this passage.

which identify St. Paul with the various and much debated themes commonly associated with him by protestant theologians, demonstrates how plainly he supplied the main outline of Teilhard's interpretation. This as we have seen is evident and admitted in the whole content of *Le Milieu*. It is also manifest in the concluding and specifically Christian sections of *The Phenomenon*. But it is at the various stages of his life as set out by Cuénot that his progressive expansion of the Pauline vision becomes clearest. And this is not only to be seen in his increasing emphasis upon the all-including and Christ-filled community.

Teilhard had grown up with a conviction of the essential identity of the God of nature and the God of Christendom, and with a consequent appreciation of the Pauline significance of the words " in Christ ". His long experience of war had disclosed not only the widespread indifference to religion in the majority of his comrades but the worth and capabilities, indeed the heroisms so freely displayed by them all. But the intimate disclosure of his views in *Genèse* which anticipate most of his later developments show that during that time he had not yet discovered the full significance for him of St. Paul's cosmic teaching. When he got established in the Far East he reached a similar but more explicit conclusion. After the Pan-Pacific Congress in December 1926 at Peking he wrote that in spite of all the talk about partnership there seemed to be very rarely any strong sense of a really shared humanity : " there is ", he concluded, " only one contact that cannot fail to draw men into unity and that is the contact of the whole man with the whole man " (cf. Cuénot, p. 104, letter of December 1926). And two months later he wrote again, " I am dreaming of a sort of Book of the Earth in which I would speak not as a Frenchman or in any sectional interest but as Man or indeed Earth-born. I would like to speak of the confidence, the ambitions and the resources but also the deceptions and anxieties and bewilderment of the man who becomes conscious of the destinies and interests of the Earth, that is of all humanity. I would not try to accommodate myself to the ebb and flow of popular ideas but only to express what I feel. I would like to make plain my faith in human work and human unity, my anger against the compartments and ceilings which isolate fragments of spirits destined to be joined together, our deception in seeing ourselves imprisoned in a cell whose limits exhaust us, our anguish in seeing ourselves alone, every one of us, in astronomical space. It seems to me that we have here a vast range of feeling and thought which no one faces because it seems foolish to do so but which is as strictly objective as any family or social business. If I could manage to put this across, it would be a little like the book of my life " (Cuénot, pp. 104–5). And so he wrote *Le Milieu divin*.

Some nine years later, after the adventure of the Yellow Cruise and his discovery of the Buddha of Jade, he confessed to his friend Abbé Breuil that he " loved it because it had told him of something that Christendom must annex ".[1] He had previously written : " I feel more and more strongly the need to free our religion from everything that is specifically mediterranean." [2] Eastern religions might be out of date and decrepit but " we cannot picture humanity as permanently imprisoned in a strait-jacket of precepts and suppose that this represents the whole range of Christendom " (Cuénot, p. 172, letter of 1938). It is not unfair to state that Chou-Kou-Tien and Peking did for him what Corinth and Ephesus did for St. Paul ; it gave him the material for a new understanding of the scale and quality of the human community ; constrained him to rethink and restate his vision of God and of the past, present and future of his universe ; and suggested both the direction of action for and the immediacy of its Christification. And the result was *The Phenomenon of Man*.

Before the outbreak of the Second World War he had dreamed of a plain statement of this full Christian faith and

[1] Cf. Cuénot, p. 171, in March 1935.
[2] Letter to Breuil, 27th May, 1923, and above, p. 85.

had even circulated cyclostyled copies of it, but his virtual imprisonment in China, though it gave him much enforced leisure for wide reading and thought, did not result in any great alterations or additions to his general view of the cosmogenesis. He had already, as we have seen, both by constant quotation, from the Latin Vulgate and in his own tongue, of the great texts of St. Paul in Romans chapter viii, Philippians ii, Colossians i and ii and Ephesians i-iv, made plain his concentration upon the cosmic Christ ; he had accepted the convergence of mankind towards a Christian community as the present phase of evolution ; had welcomed D-day as " a relief but not a joy, for in itself here and now this brutal victory of man over man is no victory for humanity" (Cuénot, p. 305) ; and had returned to France to attempt to work out his vision in terms of the practical problems of the post-war world.

His first attempt was to get permission to publish his books. The *Phenomenon* was revised and again submitted to the verdict of Rome. In 1948 he went himself to the Holy City in the hope of an opportunity to present his knowledge of the importance of evolution and the influence of the new humanism and his material for dealing with the issue. He was given no access to any competent theologians and went away convinced that Rome was still living as if Galileo had never been born and that there were two different Christianities, one of disdain for this world and of escape from it, the other of progress and consummation (Cuénot, pp. 311–16). A few of his Catholic friends realised the relevance and urgency of his work ; France elected him as a non-resident member of the Institut.

So like St. Paul when rejected by his own people, Teilhard also turned to the Gentiles. He had always realised that in a special sense his science gave him a mission to them ; and in Paris the creation of Unesco provided a particular opportunity. His comment upon the personnel, " the curse of Unesco is that it took its start with a staff of men chosen for their social position without critical consideration of their human capacity for vision " (Cuénot, p. 362 n.) shows a shrewdness which was and is abundantly justified. But they professed to deal with racial problems and the rights of man ; and on this theme he was an expert with a world-wide reputation and an outstanding record of successful experience. So he wrote first some reflections on the relation of the individual to the community and then a full and, as Cuénot testifies, outstanding letter to Torrès Bodet, examining the whole question of contacts between races and insisting that equality if this means identity of gifts is false and foolish, that what he calls " complementarity by convergence " is the true basis for co-operation, and that the essential preliminary in our present situation is not to plan in terms of races or countries but of the globe, not to insist on the greatest possible freedom for the individual, but to define the conditions in which the inevitable socialisation of man can be so achieved as to exalt in each of us not his autonomy but his " uncommunicable singularity " (Cuénot, pp. 362–4). " We must personalise the collectives and inspire individualistic democracies with a collective conscience."

Here also his work seems to have had no sort of effect upon " the chatter, the expediencies and sentimentalities about human organisation " ; indeed its only result—and it was perhaps the best possible—was his introduction to and friendship with Sir Julian Huxley. If only Gallio and St. Paul could have met outside the proconsul's court at Corinth, history might have been changed !

As it was, in spite of the frustration and seeming failure of the last sad years, Teilhard's final utterance gives a particular and very relevant precision to his life's work. He sees that the newly defined anthropology with its universal scope and cosmic significance is a prelude to a new Christology ; that St. Paul's vision of the " Christus consummator ", the mystic Christ, in whom " dwells all the totality of the Godhead incorporate " (Col. ii. 9) has a relationship, a parity, an

Teilhard and St. Paul

identity with the cosmic goal postulated by science as the aim of evolution (Cuénot, p. 450). Christ is become cosmic, the cosmos is being Christified. His last writing *Le Christique* translates for us the Pauline apocalypse into a precise and contemporary form.

CHAPTER NINE

TEILHARD AND THE PROBLEM
OF EVIL

UNTIL WE CAN GET some official explanation from the Roman authorities as to their reasons for forbidding Teilhard to publish or apparently even to discuss philosophy—and this we shall never receive in full—we can only conjecture from his own writings and to a less extent from his orthodox critics what are the theological points at which his position is liable to objection.

One of these is obviously the point on which he has supplied long and careful notes—his inability to support the biblical account of the origin of mankind from a single pair. His own emphasis, in all cases of the appearance of a new species, is on its slow and inconspicuous growth : unlike many of his Mendelian contemporaries he attaches little importance to mutations and never, I think, refers to the theories of large-scale jumps (or onto-mutations as Professor A. M. Dalcq of Brussels calls them) put forward by many distinguished European biologists. But he is nevertheless careful to insist that though the palaeontologist can only presume to deal in " mass " movements, a closer or contemporary study might disclose that the new development actually first occurred in a single pair of individuals. He definitely prefers Dr. Leakey's [1] man

[1] He mentions Leakey's discovery of a " human " jaw at Kanam in 1932 (cf. Cuénot, p. 336), and refers to it as Acheulean and the earliest known hominid (p. 390). Leakey's subsequent discoveries have confirmed the claim that Africa is the cradle of man ; cf. his report on the beds in the Olduvai Gorge, Tanganyika, delivered on 24th February 1961.

of Tanganyika as the oldest known member of the genus Homo, and Africa rather than Asia as the first home of humanity. And it is fair to say that he generally writes as if the line between Australopithecus and Zinjanthropus, which is for him the line between animal and man, was probably crossed not once for all but often during long periods of time and in a number of areas.

But for religion the problem is not affected by the precise method or deviation of the change, but by our verdict upon its character. The stories in Genesis accepted as factual by the Jewish-Christian tradition give an interpretation of man's unique sense of moral responsibility, of consequent obligation for his acts, of shame for the misuse of choice, and of guilt for the effects of wrong-doing. That man's emergent consciousness should attain a divine knowledge of good and evil and that prompted by his animal instincts he should abuse this knowledge is merely to interpret the freedom and selfconsciousness of his human status. Plainly this involves the attainment of what Lloyd Morgan calls a " self of contemplation " in addition to the " self of enjoyment " which is his sub-human inheritance : man, perhaps alone among the creatures of earth, can, so to say, confront his environment with detachment, can experience the overwhelming impact of it with a response of adoration and awe, and in so doing can also discover his own solitariness and need. This is the distinctive human birthright : it is also the fact which makes us affirm that Homo is not primarily either " sapiens " with Linnaeus or " faber " with Bergson but " adorans ", a worshipping animal—" Homo spiritualis " as Teilhard's friend, Édouard Le Roy, called it.[1]

Such an event is naturally estimated by the prevailing habit of mind of its interpreters. The modern evolutionist, whether Teilhard or Sir Julian Huxley, sees it as the outstanding achievement, the present climax of the process—the point at which the living organism began to assume a dominant share in the control of its own development. He sees it as the birth of the

[1] Cf. his *Introduction à l'étude du problème religieux*, pp. 153-4.

noosphere, the beginning of a new and unique epoch, and as such the supreme example of real progress.

Our Jewish ancestors with the intense awareness of the Law which their history and culture and religion had combined to instil, and of which the experience of the Exile in Babylon had taught them the special and segregating influence, told the story in terms of the Fall. God the Maker of a good world and of man's paradise in Eden had planned perfect innocence for his human creatures and commanded them to forgo the knowledge which would involve responsibility. The nostalgia of the dispossessed for the womb and pre-natal innocence was strong upon the authors of Genesis. The serpent, their animal forbear, was a suitable scapegoat, woman the inevitable victim. So Adam fell, and a life of exile and toil closed by death was his punishment. The dualism and demonology of their Persian overlords transformed the Serpent, or the Satan of the Book of Job, into Ahriman, Mephistopheles, the Arch-fiend, and the world, no longer God's good creation, became a battlefield from which a successful revolution was ejecting the divine, and in which his followers were a hopeless and impotent minority. That is the picture which much recent Biblical theology accepts and insists upon.

It is natural that man as he grows into fuller sensitiveness should be more deeply aware of the pain and evil of his state, of the seeming indifference of the universe, of the cruelty and devilries of human behaviour, and if he is honest of his own frustrations, failures and shame. Especially in times of calamity he is mocked by the supposed goodness of the world and stung into rebellion by the odious complacency of the prosperous. The earth for him is a vale of tears, progress on it an illusion, human effort a vanity, righteousness a lie, and the Kingdom of Heaven a Utopian fantasy. If he is a Christian he can only await the moment when God will fulfil his purpose and bring this world to its end. Reports to the World Council of Churches, lectures in theological colleges, sermons and addresses to all sorts and conditions of men have been in

the last twenty years directed almost exclusively to the re-
covery of a sense of sin. It has been difficult not to feel that
for the Churches of to-day faith, hope and charity have been
replaced by fear, despair and denunciation.

In fact the generation that had been born into the glamour
and blood-baths of 1914 to 1918 had grown up in the dis-
illusionments of the 1920s and the Fascism and Nazism of the
1930s, and so came on to Eichmann and his Ziklon or McCarthy
and his blacklists and the Churchmen who suggest that nuclear
annihilation may be God's will for his world. So the nightmare has proceeded. And the consequence has been a new
cleavage between religion and the outlook that underlies
modern thought and action at its best.

To this situation comes the impact of Teilhard de Chardin
with its fulfilment of the great theological and scientific tradition that derives from the Gospels and St. Paul, from the
Greek Logos-doctrine of the first three centuries and for us
in Britain from the Christian Platonism of the seventeenth
century, restated by F. D. Maurice and the succession which
links him with Lloyd Morgan, John Oman and William
Temple. Teilhard's full-scale interpretation of cosmic evolution in terms of the universal Christ disposes at once of the
versions of creation and fall which depose God from his world
and assign to man the power to frustrate God's purpose, and
to Satan the role of Lord of the Earth. With his vision of a
universe measured in light-years and even so unbounded, of
an earth in which succeeding realms bathysphere, lithosphere,
hydrosphere, atmosphere and stratosphere (*Phenomenon*, p. 68)
give rise to its biosphere and noosphere, and of the immense
onward and upward movement manifested throughout its
history, the old dualisms of matter and mind, body and spirit,
God and devil are plainly transcended. In such a setting the
denial of progress becomes an impossible arrogance : " Has
it even occurred ", asks Teilhard, " to those who say that the
new generation, less ingenuous than their elders, no longer
believes in a perfecting of the world, that if they are right all

spiritual effort on earth would be virtually brought to a stop ?"
(l.c. p. 232). Surely no Christian can deny his conclusion
that "If progress is a myth, our efforts will flag. With that
the whole of evolution will come to a halt—because we are
evolution," and "All conscious energy is, like love (and because it is love), founded upon hope." We are "saved by
hope", and the sort of despair so prevalent among us is in
fact a repudiation of salvation. It is an apostasy.

Nor is it in any way a valid protest to urge that Teilhard
"has no sense of sin". That is a charge easily brought against
anyone who defends the unique supremacy of God; like
pantheism it is easily applied to all who take seriously the
"divinisation" attainable in Christ and described by his
Apostle. Teilhard was, of course, fully aware of his liability
to both criticisms. Early in his work he took occasion to
protest that pantheism in the sense in which alone it is heretical
was very different from his own insistence upon the universal
presence and sustaining energy of God. "The sojourner in
the divine *milieu* is not a pantheist" (*Milieu*, p. 103). Diversity
is integrated and consummated in unity : it is not absorbed
or nullified in it. "Christianity saves the essential aspiration
of all mysticism : *to be united* (that is to become the other)
while *remaining oneself*" (p. 104). Though he admits, as any
honest student must, that on occasion St. Paul's emphasis upon
the wholeness of God, the totality of Christ, and our identification with him is so full as to suggest that for us Christification implies individual perfection, yet rightly appreciated it is
fulfilled only by membership in and total involvement with
the divine community, the "body" of Christ. For him as
for St. Paul the master-text is Ephesians iv. 13, "Until we all
come home into the oneness of our faith and our full awareness of the Son of God, into mature humanity, into the
measure of the stature of the fullness of Christ" ; and this
does not assert the equal perfection of each individual, but the
total integration of each in the full development of the whole.
Pantheism, as Dean Inge used to say, is not equivalent to

Panentheism ; the latter does not involve the former ; the
" cell" does not become the body though its whole life is
fulfilled within the body. Teilhard emphasised this distinction
in one of his last essays on the Spirit of identification and the
Spirit of unification.[1]

So with the fact of sin, he declares that as " his aim is solely
to show how all things can help the believer to unite himself
to God there is no need to concern ourselves directly with bad
actions, that is with positive gestures of disunion " (*Milieu*,
p. 58). And realising as he always does the need to take all
the field of experience into account he deals at the end of the
book with this factor in its extreme form—with the traditional
view of hell and of eternal damnation. No one reading those
pages could fail to admit that for Teilhard as for any sensitive
soul the problem of evil constitutes, with that of suffering
and even more profoundly, the paradox and testing-point
of belief.

Here, as in other matters, for example his admission that
all religious truth was revealed only through the Church (a
confession very hard for some of us to reconcile with his
general outlook), he accepted explicitly the traditional belief
in hell—though claiming that he was " forbidden to hold with
absolute certainty that any single man has been damned "
(*Milieu*, p. 141). Moreover, although he admits to praying
that the flames may never touch anyone, he reaches for his
own mind a recognition that somehow " the damned are not
excluded from the Pleroma . . . they lose it but are not lost
to it " (p. 142), and does not find this an insurmountable
obstacle. And as such though we may be unable to follow
him, we have no ground for denying his sense of sin—still
less for insinuating that his faith is shallow or incomplete.
Those who feel that the primary quality of Christ is " to seek
and to save that which is lost " (Lk. xix. 11) will share the
conviction that since divinisation is ultimately universal, eternal
damnation as commonly understood must remain for us a

[1] Cf. *Letters from a Traveller*, p. 302 and note.

contradiction in terms. Gehenna is surely the destruction of that which has forfeited all value, the rubbish dump of Jerusalem, not the everlasting torture-chamber. Immortality is not a physical condition of individual existence but a relationship with God and the community.

What we must state is rather that the language of pessimism, the insistence that for the Christian repentance begins with conviction of sin, is probably never and certainly not necessarily or always the truth. It is indeed according to the Gospels clear that the message of Jesus differed precisely in this from that of his forerunners and from the majority of his fellow-Jews. For them the first duty was to recognise and renounce evil : for him it is always to see and acknowledge God. The kerygma is not " Wash you, make you clean " but " The Kingdom of God is at hand. Repent and believe." The sequence of the Lord's Prayer is proof enough—and in the main it has been followed in all the collects and intercessions of Christendom. Our service begins with worship —with our Father and his will, not with ourselves or even our neighbours. It is only when we have seen God that we can genuinely cry, " Depart from me for I am a sinful man, O Lord " (Lk. v. 8). It is only in the light of that vision that sin is seen in its real enormity, but also in a true perspective. And so seen, it no longer produces a morbid obsession. Like Jesus we can confront evil as an intruder, an outrage, a perversion ; and so can overcome and repair and heal. Like St. Paul we can become so filled with faith and awareness of God that there is no room for sin : pride has been broken, self-will no longer dominates, we can experience the freedom which St. Augustine defined as " the blessed constraint from doing wrong ". Teilhard claims in *Le Milieu* that his concern does not admit of detailed discussion of evil : his life, according to the universal testimony of his friends and of his works, was similarly preoccupied with God. " No man can serve two masters " (Matt. vi. 24 and Lk. xvi. 13) : by the law of reversed effort too much anxiety about avoiding sin, as most of us know by experience, easily produces the very disease which it dreads.

In this seemingly ambivalent world with its strange and terrifying chequer-work of good and evil as the dominant pattern not only of its physical nature but of our innermost experience, we are all of us tempted to accept the conventional dualism and adopt the cynic's attitude of detachment. In the days of my youth there was a habit of showing us a chess-board and asking : " Do you see this as white on black or as black on white ? " The question, for some of us at least, goes deep. Do we as the background of our thinking regard the world in terms of black and white, of good and evil, equally and essentially divided ? Do we see it as Christian theology has from time to time seemed to see it, as the realm of good or of evil ? Or do we, as is the modern fashion, regard it as inevitably under present conditions piebald ? For vast numbers of us this last conviction seems the only true realism. They would reject the doctrine that it is in itself totally corrupt : this is morbid : certain values cannot be denied, and " to each his own sacraments ". But they would equally reject any belief that it is or could be the Kingdom of God as utopian and escapist : if there is any possibility of its cleansing this cannot be achieved (some would say cannot be advanced) by any human effort. One day God will bring the present world to an end—and then . . . ?

Now to Teilhard, as to all saints and very certainly to Jesus and to St. Paul, such an analogy is false. The world is not a chess-board, nor mankind the pawns upon it. Material assimilations and imagery of this kind, attractive and ready-to-hand as they are, provide a wholly inadequate picture of the realities of personal life and of the environment in which that life is set. We, human beings, are not pawns or robots, cogs on a wheel or hands in a factory. We are persons and our world is personal through and through. Even the analogy of the drama, though as an art-form it is perhaps our most appropriate mirror, is inadequate and misleading. " All the world's a stage " is the cynic's illusion—at its best a symbolism like many others aesthetic or intellectual, but plainly a scaling-down of our full experience, a translation into a lower category of a reality which in the last resort can be lived but not, on its own level, put adequately into words or even simulated by action. To accept evolution as Teilhard has done and as we others have tried to do is to transcend the fragmented aspects of our experience, these " broken bits of being ", and to see life steadily and whole. We must if we are to be fully human be concerned not only with the pieces of mosaic but with the total picture that they compose. The parts are only meaning-ful in the whole ; and the whole is neither black nor white but the " many-coloured wisdom of God ", the light of the spectrum, the Pleroma.

In consequence of this awareness, this relatively new aware-ness, of the scale and quality of the cosmogenesis to which we belong, our whole traditional idea of life aesthetic, intellectual and moral has to be re-expressed. We have to adjust our interpretations of it in relation to its wholeness and to our own personality, to the consciousness that we are not only diverse individuals but members of an integrated and universal community. In the first case it must be expressed in terms of being, of our whole active and passive lives. Then perhaps we can go on to recondition our art and thought and ethics. This is the immense task that awaits us ; and the glimpses that we get of its quality, striking in upon our constant discoveries of the irrelevance of our traditional standards and methods, are responsible for the almost universal bewilderment of the young.

It is his contributions to this situation that give Teilhard's work its particular significance. In interpreting evolution he has carried the ideas of continuity and emergence to a fuller expression : in theology he has restated in a wider context the cosmic vision of St. Paul. But in addition he has fastened upon what seem to be the essential immediacies of our present adventure, the two aspects of a coherent reply to the challenge of our modern need. He has insisted upon the abandonment of the traditional antitheses and so upon the divinisation of the secular equally with the religious, in our whole life active and passive. And he has insisted not only that the individual must find himself in the socialisation that modern achievement has made possible, but that this process of world-wide integration can only be advanced by the sharing of a common devotion, by a love which neither exploits nor sentimentalises, by a life hid with Christ in God and therefore increasingly aware of and involved in the cosmic movement of which it is a part.

Teilhard's confession of faith dating from July 1933 and printed by Cuénot on pp. 268-9 summarises his convictions. " We can be fundamentally happy only in a personal union with something personal (with the personality of everything) in everything. This is the ultimate appeal of what we call ' love '. In consequence the essential quality of the joy of life discloses itself in the knowledge or feeling that in everything that we taste, create, undertake, discover or suffer in ourselves or in others, in every possible line of life or death, organic, social, artistic or scientific, we are increasing gradually and are ourselves gradually incorporated in the growth of the universal soul or spirit." For this conviction all that is needed is an impassioned human heart and the acceptance of three points :

(1) That Evolution or the birth of the universe is by nature convergent not divergent, making for a final unity ; (2) that this unity, built up gradually by the world's labour, is by nature spiritual—spirit being understood *not* as a withdrawal from but as a transformation or sublimation or culmination of matter ; (3) that the centre of this spiritualised matter, of this totality of what is by nature spiritual, must in consequence be supremely conscious and personal : the Ocean which gathers all the spiritual tides of the universe is not only something but someone : he is in himself face and heart. If one accepts these three points the whole of life, including death, becomes for each one of us a discovery and continual conquest of a divine

and irresistible Presence. This Presence illuminates the secrecies and inmost depths of everything and every man around us. We can attain a full realisation not a simple enjoyment of everything and every man. And we cannot be deprived of it by anything or anyone. That is Teilhard's creed.

And if we are to express it theologically we find him convinced that evil is no accident or regrettable mistake. We have no right to suppose that God would have created a world without evil and suffering : they are, however we explain it, an integral part of the process. All we can say is that the world is so constructed that evil and death occur in it. " Suffering", said Teilhard in his *La Vie cosmique* of 1916, " is the consequence and the price of the labour of development." " Creation groans and travails until now," as St. Paul put it,[1] " Creation, Incarnation, Redemption, each marking a stage in the divine operation, are they not three phases indissolubly joined in the manifestation of the divine ? "[2]

---

[1] Rom. viii. 22.
[2] *L'Âme du monde* (1918), cf. Tresmontant, pp. 119–21.

CHAPTER TEN

THE CHALLENGE OF TEILHARD'S CHRISTIQUE

THE PRIMARY, and perhaps for the Anglo-Saxon world the most remarkable, fact about Teilhard de Chardin is that his brilliant and coherent interpretation of the universe should have been written by a priest and a Jesuit, and that it is there-fore centred upon, permeated by and consummated in the fact of Christ. He is not, like most of us Christians, one who forming on scientific principles a theory of evolution and the cosmos then tries to find room in it for religion and for Christianity. We do so by various modes ; either by select-ing out of the phenomena of science such elements as show resemblance or suggest analogies to Christian values ; or by positing a supernatural realm largely independent of us and of this world to which nevertheless we have access, or by maintaining that in the person of Christ two distinct and even contrasted natures, one of them wholly external to us, are manifested ; or by whatever other device, or ingenuity of thought, we may keep revelation and nature, God and man, resolutely distinct and justify our own double loyalties. Teil-hard, though he never repudiates the third of these possibilities (which is accepted by credal authority since the fifth century), has his own way of dealing with them. His approach to Christ makes them impossible ; for it is not by way of an emotional experience, nor of a reasonable hypothesis, nor of a challenging ideal. To him Christ is a fact ; he has grown up into and accepted evolution ; he has also and in precisely the same way accepted Christ. The two essential data of his experience have developed in him side by side, totally accepted and indivisibly united. As we have seen, *Le Cœur de la matière* traces process and result precisely.

We have already considered what Teilhard meant by Christ, by his living presence, his universal actuality, his cosmic significance. Like St. Paul, Teilhard saw all things as " in Christ "—and that not figuratively but factually. For him Christ was and is *Le Milieu divin*, the light and life and love of the world ; and evolution, the cosmogenesis, is the Christification of all things. And his primary evidence of this is that he not only said it but lived it. This is what compels all his readers to face the issue. To do so is the only honest course, even if the mere idea of its reality seems almost beyond our comprehension—if, as is surely the case, we are aware that our own Christianity, genuine and sincere as we believe it to be, has not this complete and all-absorbing quality. The matter demands examination.

And first there are three mistakes that we must not make about the interpretation of his *Christique*.

Teilhard may truly be called a mystic, one who saw and experienced not only the cosmic emotion of Wordsworth and the nature-mystics, the sense of a presence permeating all things, in which we could experience an ecstasy at once of union and of adoration, but also the equally vivid awareness of one's own solitariness and creaturehood and need. This Teilhard manifestly knew : it is, in some degree, universal to mankind and the characteristic of all religion. But for the majority even of mystics it is a transient and occasional moment, for many as for Plotinus uniquely memorable and infinitely precious ; and even so, as Teilhard himself insisted, evidence of a unification of the self obtainable most easily if on a lower level by abstraction from the workaday world and withdrawal of contact and attention into a complete non-attachment. Teilhard in his first-hand knowledge of Eastern religion had studied this type of experience very closely ; and his thoughts upon it are set out in his lecture in Paris (Cuénot, pp. 174-5) and in a form similar to and perhaps influenced by his compatriot E. Murisier [1] who sharply distinguished the negative mysticism of " subtraction " from the positive and inclusive fulfilment reached not by detachment from the world but by integrated and sublimated activity within it. Teilhard, though not wholly condemning the *Via negativa* or (I think) examining the extent to which it has invaded Christian mysticism, refused to give it place in the fully transformed life which he saw as only fulfilled when the whole sphere of human activity was known to be capable of divinisation. He recognised and rejected the mistake, so often and so prominently endorsed, of identifying non-attachment with agapé. If we call him a mystic we must recognise that there is nothing of escapism in his experience, that though he recognises the value of discipline and contemplation and speaks sympathetically of Jains and Buddhists, he protests that Nirvana is not Christification, nor is the way of renunciation in itself the road to the Incarnate life. In view of the widespread confusion of mysticism with other-worldliness we must protest against those who call Teilhard a mystic and so suggest his abstention from a " realistic " way of " *action* ". There is nothing in his awareness of unity or of God to suggest the effect of Mescalin or of autosuggestion : he was saved from it by his own birthright and by the influence of Le Roy and Blondel.

The second misunderstanding arises out of what is best described as the historical problem. It is the issue debated in England fifty years ago in the question " Jesus or Christ ? " Do the Christian religion and experience centre upon Jesus the Son of Man, of Nazareth and Jerusalem, described for us primarily in the Synoptic Gospels, whose ministry of teaching and healing, whose crucifixion and resurrection established the claim that he was God's Messiah, the unique representative of Man to God and of God to Man, and whose earthly life was at once the fulfilment and the permanent norm of human

[1] Cf. *Maladies du sentiment religieux*, pp. 51-72.

aspiration and the one final and perfect revelation of deity ? Or in proclaiming him as Christ do we expand and extend his quality and significance far beyond the span of events described in the Gospels and accept him as the embodiment of a life not only here and now accessible to us, but capable of illuminating and directing all our adventures into realms of experience and action vastly different from those of the first Christian century ? We can find men and women of both types within Christendom to-day—those whose lives are dedicated to a Jesus-worship concentrated upon the Gospel picture, and for whom the example there recorded is the sufficient centre of their religious life, and others for whom the Christ though first revealed in the historic time and events of the Gospels is acknowledged as personifying human perfection in its every aspect, the symbol of the divine in its fullness for whom Jesus remains as the primary and unique manifestation, but as one whose status has been more and more enlarged with the growth of our powers and who is for many of us wholly freed from the limitations of a single lifetime on earth and any restrictive identification with its transient events.

For those who recognise this distinction it may be natural to argue that admittedly Teilhard was not a historian nor in the technical sense a New Testament scholar, that as his visit to Rome made clear he is not sensitive to the glamour of the past or particularly attracted by its romance or majesty, and that in his relation to Christ it is with the personification of the divinised humanity rather than with the Jesus of history that he is concerned ; that in fact Christ means for him the consummation of the religious and personal community towards which evolution is developing. If so, we may well ask whether this does not justify us in accepting his interpretation of the cosmic process but refusing to identify it with the language, dogmas and institution of the Church. Teilhard was, of course, vividly aware of this problem, which had been raised by French Modernists far more acutely and controversially than was the case in England : indeed in one of his last letters he expressed the wish to devote his last years to it.[1]

As we have seen in considering his debt to Blondel,[2] Teilhard had found Christ from a standpoint that transcended the problems and enquiries that arise in part at least from differences of human insight, temperament and intelligence. Convinced as they were of the cosmic significance and universality of their Lord the two friends realised that though accurate theological definition was a necessary element in religion such interpretation could not fully represent and must not be allowed to restrict the grace of God or man's experience and response to it. Teilhard, like Blondel, could not accept the insistence that the work of redemption in Jesus Christ is limited to the relatively small circle of those who know the message of the Gospel [3]—though his distress over the deaths of his non-Christian friends showed that this did not imply any doubt of the value of membership in the Church. Themselves holding firmly to the truth of their own convictions they could yet recognise the plain propriety of differences of interpretation and looked beyond the complexity of the world to its convergence in an experience of Christ surpassing all that had yet been revealed. In religion as in life the creative process involved and enabled a movement onward and upward ; and by putting into action our " full knowledge " of Christ we should enable his grace to guide us into new realms of maturity and " amorisation ". Beyond and out of our divisions lay the assurance of " the peace that passeth understanding ".

This particular dilemma " Jesus or Christ " has in fact already been answered when we discussed Teilhard's connection with St. Paul ; for it amounts to a restatement of the position taken up by those scholars who maintain that the

---

[1] *Letters from a Traveller*, p. 347, letter of 3rd November 1953.

[2] Cf. above, pp. 41-2.

[3] For Blondel cf. his discussion with Wehrlé in *Au cœur de la crise moderniste*, pp. 354-6.

Apostle on his own admission had little interest in the earthly life of Jesus and in fact replaced the religion of the Gospels by his own vision and interpretation of the cosmic Christ. We have agreed that Teilhard has a very evident and accurate appreciation of the full presentation of the Pauline Christology as expressed in the three epistles, Philippians, Colossians and Ephesians, but have maintained that this represents the result of a traceable and consistent process of interpretation which started from the impact of Jesus upon him, an impact such as St. Mark and the earliest kerygma first recorded. The fact is that Jesus from the beginning of his ministry convinced his hearers that here was something new, original, compelling, something for which they had no appropriate interpretation. They could only apply to it the terms suggested by previous experience—and find them manifestly and almost absurdly inadequate. St. Paul was merely continuing the process to which Teilhard has now added a new level of definition. Experience will test, is already testing, the extent to which his version of truth is consistent with the past, present and future of human evolution and Christian insight into it. Meanwhile it is scarcely honest to dismiss Teilhard's *Christique* on the ground that it follows the continuously enlarged apprehension of Jesus which began at his first public appearance at Capernaum.

The third objection naturally arises over the practical consequences and applications of his message, and particularly of the increasing socialisation and totalisation which he sees as the fulfilment at the modern level of the vital principle of convergence. In his whole vision of the future, and especially in his discussion with Sir Julian Huxley and Sir Charles Darwin recorded by Dr. Cuénot, pp. 366–70, he sets out the human aspect of the Christogenesis described in the final sections of the *Phenomenon* ; and it involves the attainment of unanimity, of co-operation and of world-wide community. How far in view of the strength of individualism and of its dread of Marxism, of the tensions still occasioned by race and class and sex, and of the obsessive power of militarism, nationalism and xenophobia can any such universal trend towards what Smuts called holism be accepted ? Is it possible even in Christianity to replace the concept of individual salvation by the belief that only in corporate Christification can the individual reach his fulfilment ?

Before we dismiss Teilhard as a Utopian dreamer with no sense of sin or as a fellow-traveller of Communism with no love of liberty we must look more closely at the type of sociology that he advocates and in fact succeeds in defining. In his later writings and correspondence he makes it quite clear that the classic summary of the French revolution, liberty, equality, fraternity, whatever it meant to the idealists of the eighteenth century is not now a true picture of the Christian community. For liberty has come to mean " freedom to do what I like and to possess what I can pay for ", and this is surely the road not to heaven but to hell : and equality means " one man one vote " which Dean Inge rightly defined as belief in " the plenary inspiration of the odd man ". Teilhard has, at first sight, very little in common with modern democracy and still less with Western individualism. But his socialism is precisely that of John Malcolm Ludlow and Frederic Denison Maurice—perhaps indeed nearer to the royalism of the latter than the republicanism of the former. He does not start with the social order, with organisation and constitutions and forms of government, but with the " new spirit ", the Holy Spirit, of which these will then be the embodiment and means of expression.

Liberty is for him as it was for St. Augustine *beata necessitas non peccandi*, " the blessed constraint of not doing wrong ", and this is the inevitable condition of life in Christ " whose service is perfect freedom ". Like St. Paul he conceives of life which is not as most Christians regard it a ceaseless battle with the world, the flesh and the devil, but as so thrilled with the love of God that evil is crowded out, so inspired by the full knowledge or total consciousness of Christ that in his presence there is no room for sin nor any need of rules and punishments. The Law is only the servant to take the child to school ; the " teacher " as Clement of Alexandria called him is the Christ.

And equality is not the pretence that there is no such thing as race and class and sex or that these conditions do not constitute differences. For Teilhard, though they are real and at present at least important and valuable, they are not (even sex !) final and permanent ; they add variety to life and help to determine function. But in the community they must not, and rightly recognised cannot, diminish the full status of the splendid co-operation that unites them. Each and all are in Christ, members of his body, fulfilling themselves in his life and nature and activity. Again St. Paul supplies the analogy : the foot must not say to the hand nor the eye to the ear " you are not of the body " nor any of them to God " why hast thou made me thus ? " There is place for all, and need for all. Each has a special vocation and is equal to all others in his discharge of it. Here again is a criterion for the new humanity. If all life is a sacred ministry then the oppressions and restrictions, the corruptions and the jealousies of the body politic are gangrenes that poison the whole community, they are treasons against the common life, practices incompatible with its health and joy, tragedies of wastage and maladjustment.

Teilhard in fact has succeeded in fulfilling his conviction that the whole cosmic process is an evolution ; that the primary constituent, the radiant energy of the universe is so constituted that at every level of its existence a measure of convergence appropriate to that level prepares for and makes possible the attainment of a higher, more complex and conscious, state ; and that with the attainment of the noosphere personal qualities assume a precise and predominant place in it : it becomes a convergence towards a universal and unanimistic community concentrated upon and fully integrated in Christ. The ideas outlined by thinkers like Lloyd Morgan and Smuts have taken shape and power from being more fully explored at their crucial point, the coming of man, more adequately integrated by explicit identification with the realised presence of the divine.

We have examined the three aspects of his cosmic philosophy and found that the Christ-centredness far from being a concession to mystic emotion or to theological tradition, or to the collectivism of our age, is not only relevant and formative but primary and essential. When in *La Religion du personnel* (Cuénot, pp. 239–40) he writes, " The essence of Christianity is neither more nor less than the belief in the Unification of the world in God by the Incarnation," he expresses the conviction upon which his whole scientific-religious philosophy is based, and when he adds " *Alone*, unconditionally alone, in the world to-day, Christianity shows itself able to reconcile, in a single living act, the All and the Person " and " Through it the principal axis of evolution truly passes " (p. 298) he confronts us with his basic affirmation.

The challenge of his claim must be honestly faced by all of us who realise the merits of his philosophy but are not committed to obedience to the Catholic Church or able to accept all that its authority demands. Teilhard himself obviously finds certain elements in orthodoxy hard and unpalatable. There is evidence of a strict self-discipline in his very moving pages at the end of *Le Milieu* where he deals with evil and with eternal damnation, as also in his attitude towards some of the imagery of traditional doctrine and hagiology. We can perhaps legitimately feel that ideas of infallibility and of unquestioning obedience which many of us regard as in conflict not merely with our interpretation of the evidence but with our whole concept of God's nature and dealings with us, were for him too the subject of much honest hesitation—that he would at least have understood the genuineness of our objections to them. We cannot on these matters lightly plead " invincible ignorance " or dismiss them as unimportant. But we can, most of us, honestly say that it is not on these grounds that his " Christique " is difficult for us. If and so far as his Christology is that of St. Paul we can inspect it intellectually and try to apply it in our lives and conduct. We can, or so I believe, give an answer to the Gospel question " What think ye of Christ ? " not inconsistent in intention with the New Testament.

It is when we are faced with the full content of such committal, faced not only by the utterances of Teilhard but by the quality and impact of his life that we shrink from accepting this total conformity. For him quite obviously the words " in Christ " cover his whole experience : he expresses in all his relationships the Pauline assertion " to me to live is Christ " (Phil. i. 21)—the final endorsement of the Apostle's first confession " I live, yet not I : Christ lives in me " (Gal. ii. 20). Can we with any sort of sincerity iterate such a claim ? And if not, dare we see ourselves as working towards or being accepted as followers of Teilhard's teaching ? Those in view of the scale and relevance of his work are very searching questions.

In giving our answers we must again recollect what is involved. Just because of the scope and consistency of his work we cannot appreciate or express it either by escaping from the world or by striving to dominate it and becoming " Captains of our souls " within it. It is by living in the world, serving our own portion of it, and fulfilling to the uttermost our special contribution to its welfare that we shall be following his lead, and promoting the universalising, unity and Christification of mankind. This is the incarnational principle which St. Paul was the first to announce and which almost no subsequent Christian has dared to accept. It is to attempt what Jesus alone has succeeded in accomplishing. It is to live wholly in the Kingdom of God here and now. It is to practise a realised eschatology and take our place in what James Ward called the Realm of Ends. It is to obey the word of Jesus and take up our Cross.

It is easy enough to write such words—and even to find in them now and for a time a new meaning and appeal. But we must not regard them, as too often in the past, as calling us to an individual adventure of martyrdom. For Teilhard the goal cannot be his own salvation : it is the divinisation of our world, of our activities and passivities in and with the corporate life. For him and for us, as for Jesus, the motive for sanctification is " for their sakes " and it is in and for them that the adventure must be accomplished—this adventure to which in his last work he gave the name *amorisation*.

This may at least suggest how the familiar imagery of the call can be given a prosaic and immediately mundane response. To divinise activities and passivities—and freeing ourselves from our self-obsession to take the active duty first—could we not each in our own sphere set up a definite " order " or ministry as Teilhard himself had indicated ? A small group of " disciples " who recognised that their own trade or profession could not but either promote or hinder the divinisation of society, and who began by investigating as in Christ first their own motives and practices in it and then the conditions which marred or promoted its true intention, might not only deepen their own commitment but express to others something of the true purpose of human lives and works. It would help to recover and widen the sense of vocation and to build up a company which could face the solitariness and overcome the obstacles that beset the reformer, and if the adventurers were sincere and unselfconscious might have a share in fulfilling the apostolic precept of redeeming the time.

And with this estimate and personal response might come the power to set on foot the sort of large-scale and corporate Christian movement whose first task should be to survey and report upon the whole range of problems concerned with politics, economics and citizenship. When in 1924 the British Churches co-operated in a national conference on these subjects its twelve volumes of preparatory report were the first united effort to bring the life of the community under Christian criticism. It supplied the material laid next year before the Stockholm Conference on the Life and Work of the Church and had a large influence in drawing attention to the social tensions arising out of the modern unification and inter-dependence of humanity. But it also disclosed how very wide and how largely ignored was the field of enquiry, and how narrowly Christian ethics had been confined to matters of individual responsibility and behaviour. Certainly if Teilhard's dream is to be accepted, Christendom must face the comparatively new diseases and resources of the body politic. Convergence must involve such co-operation and this must be at the level not of the mob or of the committee but of a fully Christian community.

Out of such an adventure, undertaken with the full intention to draw together all men of goodwill and, with Teilhard, to unite Christians and humanists and members of other religions on ground common to them all, might come the emergence of that Human Front for which *Sauvons l'humanité* was a plea. It might fulfil Teilhard's belief that the United Nations or at least Unesco should undertake the provision of an integrative programme for world-community, of a concentration of international research not only upon the nature and creation of such community but upon methods and institutions for its expression and organisation, and so of a sense of solidarity, trust and fellowship between the races, groups and individuals attached to it.

It is surely only by such a positive and constructive adventure that the fears and hatreds, the despair and hysteria that our new possibilities and inventions have fostered can be transformed into the " convergence " which would make our dreams come true. And of Teilhard himself we may quote the words of his English friend Dr. Tindell Hopwood, " when the history of his time comes to be written it may well be found that he did more to influence the development of French thought, and hence of European thought, than any other man of his generation ".[1]

---

[1] Cf. *Proceedings of Linnean Soc. London*, vol. 167, p. 142.

CHAPTER ELEVEN

APPENDIX:
TEILHARD AND HIS CRITICS

BEFORE TEILHARD'S DEATH and therefore before any of his religious and larger work had been published, critics from within the Church had begun the circulation of warnings against his orthodoxy. The first of these, the Abbé Louis Cognet, a devout and devoted student of ascetic theology, printed a volume, *Le Père Teilhard de Chardin et la pensée contemporaire*, in 1952, which is a good example of the reaction of the tradition. It is based upon cyclostyled copies of some half-dozen of Teilhard's writings including both *Le Milieu* and *Le Phénomène* and is admittedly the comment of an orthodox but not unsympathetic Catholic upon a world-view which at once attracts and alarms him. He realises that "contemporary thought" is based upon knowledge and an outlook which is rapidly becoming universal. He has no idea of the extent to which this knowledge challenges and is making untenable the basis of the Christian philosophy as he has received and teaches it. But he is convinced that the new is radically distorted and dangerous. So with modesty but determination, and using all the techniques of the old deductive logic he girds himself to demonstrate its errors. The effect is, to a modern, inevitably that of Haig's cavalry at Cambrai charging a well-wired machine-gun battery : "c'est magnifique mais ce n'est pas la guerre".

It is worth examining his book : nothing will show more plainly the gulf that separates Teilhard from his conservative critics, or the extent to which the tradition is irrelevant to our age.

Cognet's first and most obvious anachronism is the charge that Teilhard confuses the various compartments of knowledge : " the natural sciences are brought on to the stage under the same title as philosophy and theology : how far is it permissible to join together ideas from such diverse realms of thought" (p. 22). This is of course the typical outlook and error which has bedevilled the whole relationship between science and religion ever since Francis Bacon laid it down that whereas the New Philosophy dealt with everything that could be subjected to observation and experiment, religion lay wholly outside its purview since it was based not upon experience, but upon " the infallible oracles of God ". It is a position that for a brief period thirty years ago led some of my scientific contemporaries to maintain the autonomy and isolation of all branches of knowledge and to treat each under its own special framework of reference. A biologist must accept a purely mechanistic theory and technique ; a historian is concerned with objectively demonstrable facts ; a theologian with metaphysical principles. Every man in his time can play many parts each with its appropriate rules and standards, and these need not be mutually consistent. So the critic represents Teilhard as a quick-change actor now scientist, now poet, now thinker, now apologist ; and insinuates that he perpetually confuses one with the other.

This whole compartmentalising of life and thought, fostered as it has been by our over-specialised education, is surely a survival which the advance of modern understanding has falsified. From psychosomatic medicine to the universality of inductive methods or from the study of parapsychology to that of abstract art we are recognising the essential unity of the universe and the need to explore and employ all possible avenues for its interpretation. Ultimately truth is one and we can best approximate to it by the use of all our faculties. Teilhard's insistence upon convergence and his free employment of his full sensibility, intelligence and aspiration are the plain consequence of his belief in personality and unanimisation. He more than most sees life steadily and sees it whole.

Contrast this with his critic. Cognet still sees science as a discipline independent of philosophy and theology ; and within science similar isolated compartments are inserted. Evolution, he argues (pp. 66–8) is a theory supported almost solely by palaeontologists. Other scientists use it as a hypothesis convenient for special phenomena in limited fields. Teilhard has no right to accept it as universal.

After this charge that Teilhard has based his position upon a disputable hypothesis he goes on to assert that he leaves no room for divine transcendence. This he argues not on the ground that Teilhard should have given more space to the metaphysical theology which in fact in the *Phenomenon* he expressly points out that he is not discussing, but because in asserting the continuity of evolution he has denied the evidence supplied by man's transcendence of the animals and life's radical difference from the inanimate. By this he presumably means that Teilhard ignores the emergence of novelty [1] which is in fact untrue, and that God's transcendence is demonstrated by his interventions in creating new levels of progress.

From these two criticisms it is plain first that Cognet has no idea of the strength and variety of the evidence for evolution, nor of the extent to which the continuity of the process has been demonstrated and the origin of life explored, nor of the disaster which befalls those who try to fit God's intrusions into the gaps of our human understanding. His ignorance of biological science disqualifies him from appreciating the significance of Teilhard's work, and indeed proves that he has little understanding of contemporary or indeed of post-Darwinian thought on the whole subject.

The fact is of course that he cannot admit the reality of

[1] Yet some pages later he seems to allow for it, though he compares emergence to the fitting together of a jigsaw puzzle (p. 98).

evolution or even believe that the world is God's world. For though declaring that God is the only true being, he insists that this being finds himself confronted with another personality dedicated to evil, the Devil, the Prince of Darkness ; and that the world is a battlefield, betrayed by man's first sin into the power of God's successful rival. This is a mystery ; but all Christian tradition presents it as a dogma (pp. 108–13). Cognet protests that this dualism is not Manichaeism but his emphasis upon the personality of Satan and the enslavement to him of mankind is in fact an endorsement of the Manichaean mythology—with the damaging admission that Ahriman is inevitably doomed to defeat. We can fully share his insistence upon the exceeding sinfulness of sin : we know not only the recent and monstrous evidence of Auschwitz and Hiroshima but also the disclosures of analytical psychology as to the extent of our subconscious animalism, perverted intellects and besetting selfishness : but no one who has wrestled with the ghoulish behaviour of the insect-world as Fabre revealed it to us, or meditated on the place of struggle and pain in the story of evolution, or on the depravity of our own outlook and character will feel that to lay the blame upon the devil and invent legends to excuse God for failing to defeat him is no longer either reasonable or effective. We must not cherish Satan as the scapegoat for our sins.

Teilhard has in fact recalled us to the Pauline view of " frustration " as a divinely ordered instrument for the development of freedom and of hope :[1] It is not an accident that the Apostle sets his answer to the problem of evil as the climax of his long account of human and individual salvation, and expresses it in terms of a creative process which shall end in the splendour of the freedom of the family of God. The picture of the cosmic Christ manifested in the whole cosmogenesis and derived by Teilhard from the Epistles and especially Romans, Philippians, Colossians and Ephesians must surely

[1] Romans viii. 18–39.

take the place for our day and generation of Dante and Milton and Abbé Cognet.

This section of his criticism is an excellent example of the extent to which the traditional imagery and in consequence much of its underlying assumptions demand radical restatement. For upon his dualism follows his consequent treatment of human conduct which he defines as to fight the devil and to keep out of the world ruled by him ; of grace which is God's predetermined gift and has nothing to do with our love and service ; of salvation which though it involves membership of the Catholic Church has a purely individual meaning ; or of history which is for Teilhard a quest and adventure but for Cognet not a progress but a return to a lost paradise (pp. 181–3). Any endorsement of vision of the cosmic Christ, any hope of a world in which God shall be all in all, Cognet describes as an eschatology sufficiently disconcerting (p. 185). Of Teilhard's continual insistence upon the unifying power of love, of the convergence that love makes possible, and of the universality of the cosmic Christ Cognet does not seem to have any appreciation. His attack with its formal acceptance of the tradition of Paradise Lost and Regained, of inherited curse and supernatural grace, plainly indicates how and why the Church has lost its power to hold the best elements in the modern world. When for the first time in history man has the opportunity and the resources for controlling evolution, it is surely neither godly nor right to tell him that he is so tainted with ancestral guilt, so dominated by the Prince of Darkness, so incapable of any sort of effective service and so dependent upon the supernatural grace which only the Papal Church can mediate that he must aim to detach himself from the world. This is precisely the message of Abbé Cognet's book.

And yet its author had apparently read both the *Milieu* and the *Phenomenon* ; and so must have been aware that he was dealing with a man of saintliness as well as of sound learning. And publishing his attack in 1952 he must have known that hardly any of his readers had ever had a chance of seeing or hearing his victim's own writings.

This sort of criticism would not in itself be worth serious mention did it not represent an outlook which for all its absurdity is not only shared by some of our Protestant scholars who write about religion and science but by officials who speak with the authority of the Vatican behind them. The former of these need not seriously concern us : they belong to the period of the " great blight " when pessimism enforced by political and economic disasters led to a revival of Gnostic dualisms and other-worldlinesses which went near to banishing God from the world, denying all meaning to human effort, and identifying faith with credulity and science with material-ism. Such a phase, very vocal between 1935 and 1950, is now dated and in decline.

Much more serious is the endorsement and stricter defini-tion of Abbé Cognet's charges by semi-official if not fully authoritative Roman theologians ; for they have at least the great tradition of a rational faith and the example of the scholastic philosophers St. Albert the Great and St. Thomas Aquinas with whom Teilhard has been often compared and indeed has something in common.

Shortly after Teilhard's death the influential Roman review *La Civiltà Cattolica* printed in December 1955 an important article by a distinguished Jesuit, G. Bosio, and this was reported upon by the *Osservatore Romano* and translated into French in the next month's *Documentation Catholique*. This starts by stating that Teilhard does not regard evolution as an hypo-thesis but as a universal condition to which all theories and systems must accommodate themselves if they are to be accepted as true. " We cannot ", says Bosio, " conceal our perplexity in face of assertions so categorical." He challenges it not only by the opinions of such scientists as still treat evolution as hypothetical but by the Encyclical of Pius XII *Humani generis* which condemns anything monistic or pantheis-tic. Nicolas Corte (L. Cristiani) who comments upon this in

La Vie et l'âme de Teilhard,[1] pp. 173-7—a book which has received the *imprimatur*—points out that neither of these epithets can fairly be applied to Teilhard who nowhere explicitly repudiates dualism and frequently rejects pantheism ; Corte himself quotes from St. Augustine on Genesis to show that evolution is fully consistent with orthodoxy.[2] Later when Bosio definitely attacks *Le Phénomène* he does so on the ground that in speaking of the inwardness of things Teilhard does not definitely distinguish body from soul and that on the origin of man he does not insist upon a specific divine intervention nor upon the special creation of a single human pair nor with any sufficient emphasis upon sin, the Fall, the Devil, and our redemption.

These representatives of the traditional cosmology and demonology do not fully represent the Catholic critics and commentators. In 1956, just after the publication of *Le Phénomène*, the Éditions du Seuil issued a volume by Claude Tresmontant, a well-known student of biblical and Christian thought, *Introduction à la pensée de Teilhard de Chardin*. This is important not only as the first sympathetic statement of his characteristic ideas but as containing quotations from a number of his writings still unpublished and especially from his autobiographical confession *Le Cœur de la matière* which his friends generally agree to be invaluable for a full understanding of him. Though he begins by stating that there are three phases in Teilhard's thought, his technical palaeontology, his synthetic and scientific interpretation of the Universe and his Christ-mysticism, he deals only with the two last and never quite conveys the fact that Teilhard did not thus rigidly separate them. His account of Teilhard's Vision of the World is set out in a succession of chapters dealing with the general

[1] Translated into English with a valuable introduction by Fr. M. Jarrett-Kerr.

[2] This claim put forward by R. de Sinéty in 1930 was criticised by Dr. É. Gilson, *Introduction à l'étude de saint Augustin*, and with reference to Teilhard by Dr. G. Crespy in his recently published book discussed below, pp. 207-8, which deals with this on pp. 136-9.

character of evolution (the "stuff" and elements from hydrogen to uranium) ; the "complexity-conscience" (increasing growth and sensitiveness) ; the "cephalisation" (concentration of nerves and brain) ; the noosphere (human intellect and control) ; the point of reflection and convergence (unanimisation) ; the Omega or consummation. He attempts to present this as a phenomenology and does so with success in marking both the stages of the advance and the continuity of the process. But when he turns to the specifically religious side of it it is evident how much Teilhard's integrity of presentation suffers. He gives the impression of producing an apologetic, and rather of expressing dissent from a few details than of emphasising the consistency and therefore in many respects the novelty of Teilhard's work. Thus for example when at the end of his life [1] Teilhard came to reject the God who works from outside and independently in favour of One who works in the totality of things and by convergence and claims (justly) that this is St. Paul's meaning, Tresmontant adds a footnote indicating that this seems a forced interpretation of the Apostle.

Finally we must deal at greater length with the more subtle volume, *Dialogue avec Teilhard de Chardin*, by the Dominican scholar Olivier Rabut, published in English in June 1961 ; for this accepts much of Teilhard's thought as stimulating and full of insight, gives a detailed account of his principal works, illustrated by fairly chosen quotations, criticises them seriously and regards them on the whole as worthy of exact and expert study. His book is probably the best Catholic commentary upon him yet published. But it reveals how impossible it is for a traditionally trained mind to appreciate the changes that have come over the scientific world in the past twenty years or to accept the abandonment of the familiar dualisms and arbitrary distinctions. Teilhard is a man of independent genius, and in addition, as one of the greatest living palaeontologists has said, " a great scientist in his own

[1] Cf. *Le Cœur de la matière*, Tresmontant, p. 115.

right, and in his own field at the top " : moreover he is concerned to see the cosmos and God steadily and so far as may be whole. Rabut is a don, brought up in a strict system, applying the old categories to subjects cut up according to the old disciplines, and so too handicapped to understand or to convey the unity and coherence of a full experience. Thus for example he quotes twice [1] Teilhard's favourite illustration of the principle of emergence, but never seems to have heard of the subject or of its large contribution to evolutionary theory : so too he contrasts psychic with somatic as two totally distinct levels of being, and in consequence misinterprets Teilhard's " Withinness " and never refers to the psychosomatic outlook which has rejected the problem of what Professor Ryle calls " the ghost in the machine ".

It is I think fair to say that even from his first writings Teilhard like Lloyd Morgan or Spinoza rejected the crude antithesis of body and mind or matter and spirit or, even though with diffidence, natural and supernatural. Studying the ancient problem of the one and the many he saw both the parts and the whole, the organism and the cosmos, as entities to be regarded in their relationship. Like Smuts he constantly rejected the fallacy that when a whole had been analysed into its constituent parts these are original, or that their sum is equivalent to that from which they were derived.[2] Rabut is all for such analysis and too often accuses Teilhard of ignoring distinctions when in fact no one is more explicit in separating the various levels of existence, hylosphere, biosphere, noosphere, or in insisting upon the universality of evolution and movement or in stressing the total relevance of religion and of Christ. Thus the bulk of his elaborate criticisms of Teilhard, for example in chapters 3 and 4, are irrelevant : he has not understood the basic significance of wholeness and of emergence.

Rabut thus misses the supreme importance of Teilhard's

[1] *Dial.* pp. 37 and 94.
[2] Cf. *Phenomenon*, p. 110, etc.

work by cutting up his criticism into three strictly segregated sections, cosmology, philosophy and theology, and frequently affirming that this separation is essential to a proper treatment of the problems with which Teilhard is concerned. Teilhard by his insistence that his great book deals only with pheno-mena when it inevitably treats also of philosophy and religion is partly to blame—though it is surely obvious that no one could adequately deal with the nature of man without recog-nising that Rabut's three categories must not only be treated in combination, but are all indispensable for every aspect of the subject. Anyone who takes evolution seriously is agreed that consciousness plays an increasing and, at the human level, dominant part ; that to examine this and estimate its signi-ficance involves philosophy ; and that for any serious study of man and his influence upon the world religion is a matter of universal, if not primary, importance. Yet Rabut con-stantly criticises Teilhard for trespassing in his study of evolu-tion outside the region which he regards as peculiar to science, and also blames him for not dealing scientifically with prob-lems that he in fact treats as fundamental also for philosophy and for theology. Teilhard's work whether it deals with human origins, with the nature of community or with the universality of Christ deliberately aims at demonstrating the unity of truth and the need to take all the evidence into account. Rabut has not yet realised that the whole trend of modern science is to say *nil scibile a me alienum puto*, " I must take the whole intelligible field into my province " : ever since the new psychology won its way into the science-faculties of the universities it has been obvious that the exclusive reign of weight and measurement was over. To-day many of us, students of biology and of evolution, affirm that to exclude human history and experience, philosophy and religion from the study is to confine the field of science to technology and gadget-mongering. Indeed so far as Britain and its educational system are concerned the much vaunted cleavage between science and arts, dramatically exaggerated by a recent Rede lecturer in Cambridge, is an anachronism. It was certainly true of the public schools prior to the war of 1914. It was no longer general in the twenties. And to-day there is a wider appreciation of literature, drama, music and painting among scientists than there is of any form of science among the literary faculties. Anyone who has seen the annual exhibitions on school speech-days will realise not only how various are the activities now being pursued, but how much the old segregations are being broken down.

Equally objective and learned is the volume *La Pensée théologique de Teilhard de Chardin*, published late in 1961 by Dr. Georges Crespy, professor in the faculty of Protestant theology at Montpellier. This is confined to a thorough exposition and critical study of Teilhard's doctrinal and philosophical teaching from the standpoint of a learned and orthodox scholar representative of the Reformed rather than the Scholastic tradition, sympathetic with the New Philosophy of the Scientific renaissance but familiar with Catholic thought and well able to compare Teilhard with " the greatest doctor of the Church ", St. Augustine.

Such a criticism for one like Teilhard who was quick to admit that the spring of his thoughts and action was always "*plus sensible qu'intellectuelle* " [1] was a stringent test. We can see from the intimate accounts in his letters to his cousin Marguerite that his convictions came to him by experience and observation and were then translated carefully and with much revision into appropriate language ; but that this was not dictated by logical formulae or dogmatic rulings. Crespy's analysis is that of a systematist who applies the criteria of theological tradition, discloses the points at which Teilhard is liable to depart from it, and then adjudicates upon the extent and significance of the differences. He fully realises that the advances in scientific and psychological knowledge make the traditional methods inadequate, but while noting the points of divergence arrives at the clear conclusion that in all essentials

[1] Cf. Letter of 20th June 1916 in *Genèse*, p. 134.

Teilhard is free from anything that can properly be regarded as heresy. The fact that he follows the comparison with St. Augustine by an even longer chapter upon Dr. Bultmann and Teilhard's attitude to myth and history adds much to the scope and value of his work.

The question which his book inevitably raises is whether Teilhard can be properly judged by the criterion of the Roman and Reformed theology of the West with their legal and formal standards of conformity. To some of us, as to Dr. Gervase Mathew, his true quality resembles that of the Eastern and Origenist evolutionary philosophy, the Cappadocian fathers in their love of nature and sense of mystery and especially St. Gregory of Nyssa, and so has a basic affinity with the British tradition which may perhaps claim to be their modern representative. But in any case Dr. Crespy has made a real contribution to the final appreciation of Teilhard's orthodoxy.

It should, however, be added that Dr. Crespy, though he states that Christians normally accept the authority of the Bible or of the Tradition, fully admits that Teilhard does not primarily concern himself with either, since for him as for St. Paul and St. John faith is centred not upon them but upon the cosmic and eternal Christ. It is a pity that he does not press this admission further, but in his last chapter shows himself too close to Teilhard's Catholic critics in his emphasis upon sin and judgment—too close to the Manichaeism which St. Augustine and his followers have never quite rejected, and of which Teilhard in his last writing, *Le Christique*, warned us that it still to-day tainted, " a Gospel in which the Cross is constantly placed before our eyes to recall to us the initial failure of the world we live in ".[1]

We have hitherto been concerned with critics of Teilhard who question the adequacy or even the orthodoxy of his Christianity. They represent a large number of those for whom his thoroughgoing acceptance of evolution involves the abandonment of the traditional diabolistic dualism, of the

[1] Quoted by J. E. Bruns in *The World of Teilhard*, p. 178.

confining of the divine love to particular " elect " peoples and individuals, and of the denial of a real union of divine and human in Christ. For them God remains the infinite and wholly transcendent, whose action in the world if not altogether unpredictable yet seems to fall far short of what Jesus described as fatherhood. All attempts to see the divine as universally present, loving and sustaining his creation, rejoicing in his works, and involved in the whole process and adventure of the cosmos come under their condemnation.

Of shorter criticism and reviews bearing upon the scope of this volume the most important seems to be that of Dr. J. Needham already mentioned. For of all Englishmen Needham is probably the best equipped to appreciate the range and appraise the value of Teilhard. His own outstanding work in biochemistry starting under Sir Gowland Hopkins and expanding into an intimate knowledge of human embryology, its history and problems, his concern with religion and understanding of the appeal and limitations of Catholic Christianity, his independence of judgment and deep sociological commitments, and in particular his years of close contact with China and sympathy with Chinese science and achievements, enable him to meet Teilhard on common ground. His review of the *Phenomenon* in the *New Statesman* though it does not attempt to estimate the full range of Teilhard's thought is marked by a valuable concentration upon the essential contribution of the book, its original and abundantly valuable treatment of ideas only now beginning to emerge and still strange and difficult, upon what he regards as its lack of knowledge of the history of human culture, upon its richly intellectual and poetical restatement of the scientific view of the world, and upon the personal epic of the writer's. long and " costing " adventure towards a reconciliation of science and religion in the context of the whole universe of space and time.

Dr. Needham, though himself an eminent scientist, can appreciate Teilhard in the full range of his interests and has the

wisdom to know that any attempt to interpret man's experience of nature cannot be cut up into distinct and separately
labelled compartments. We have already seen that many of
his religious critics concern themselves not only with discussing his relation to the Christian tradition of orthodoxy
but with classifying his work in its proper department of
knowledge : is it poetry or prose, is it theology or mysticism,
is it philosophy or metaphysics ?—as if the truth and worth
of his achievement depended upon its label.

When we come to the scientists who have expressed their
views upon him, this sectarian spirit becomes still more evident,
and the recently published American volume *The World of
Teilhard* (Baltimore, 1961) is heavily weighted with it. His
friend Professor G. G. Simpson had already set the example
by summing him up as " primarily a Christian mystic and
only secondarily, although importantly, a scientist": and many
of the contributors are obviously asking not "is this true ?" but
"is it science ?" And some of them appear to suppose that if
they can show that it does not satisfy their definition of science
then it can be dismissed as irrelevant, if not indeed as an
impertinent invader of their sanctuary. Those of us who
remember the twenty years of such treatment which kept the
universities and many of the hospitals closed to psychiatry
had thought that the attempt to confine science to the realm
of physical weights and measurements had been abandoned
when that struggle ended. But in this country and still more
in America it is obvious that we have been wrong. The book
in question which contains much that is both appreciative and
valuable arrived too late for full examination. But it is good
to see that the two psychologists, Dr. Karl Stern and Dr.
James L. Foy, both castigate this exclusiveness [1]—which surely
does in effect reduce science itself to technology.

It is significant that this attitude which would deny Teilhard's claim to have followed scientific methods in his exposition of the cosmos is in fact being abandoned by men well

[1] Cf. especially pp. 40-2 and 115-16.

qualified to express views on such matters. While this chapter was being written Dr. C. H. Waddington, Professor of Animal Genetics in Edinburgh and distinguished not only in his own field of research, but for a series of books explaining the social and ethical significance of recent biological studies, was publishing *The Nature of Life* (London, 1961) in which he defines science as " the application to questions concerning the external world of *all* the major faculties which man is capable of exercising " (p. 16). He goes on to insist that science must realise that along with the analytical study of the particular items in the composition of an organism it must also pay heed to their reactions and relationships in the life of the organism as a whole and of the world to which it belongs ; and that the clash between students of the atomistic method and of the continuum is characteristic of the modern situation. He seems hardly to realise that the two—individual part and integrating community—belong together, but he insists that both modes of approach are essential. The whole book illustrates this insistence, and in its final chapter he speaks with warm approval of Teilhard and his work in regard both to the " without " and " within " of things, to the continuity of the cosmic process, and to the self-consciousness which constitutes man's special and controlling achievement.

Finally we must turn to those whose attitude towards the problems with which he is concerned makes them unable to accept or understand his position ; and as an example of them, Professor P. B. Medawar, the zoologist and Nobel prizeman, is outstanding. We have already referred [1] to his violently emotional attack upon Teilhard's character and book printed in *Mind*, which for one who usually preserves a detached and exact judgment is curiously unfair and offensive. But it is only right to go behind this outburst to the intellectual position of which it is the consequence.

Dr. Medawar is in his scientific papers and indeed his broadcasts a clear and precise essayist whose interest is in detailed

[1] In Chapter One, p. 19.

analysis on physical-chemical lines expressed in polysyllabic and highly professional language and culminating in statistical tables and mechanical diagrams. Of the value of such research and the importance within its own field of his conclusions there is no question. His paper on Lamarck, for example, printed in *The Uniqueness of the Individual*, p. 196, though not easy reading, is a definite contribution to the controversy—a careful exposition of the case that instances of the apparent inheritance of acquired characteristics do not carry the weight sometimes attached to them. In the main his work is constructive and, as the Nobel award proves, of high quality. But he is usually careful not to generalise widely from it or to attempt a positive interpretation of his general philosophy.

This is, however, indicated in a few sentences at the close of his postscript to the life of Sir D'Arcy Thompson[1] dealing with the greatest of his books, *Growth and Form*. He there wrote speaking of Thompson's influence : " Most clearly is it to be seen in the complete matter of factness with which we now accept certain beliefs that D'Arcy as a natural historian had to fight for ;[2] not merely that the physical sciences and mathematics offer us the only pathway that leads to an understanding of animate nature, but also that the true beauty of nature will be revealed only when that understanding has been achieved." These two beliefs are both dangerous half-truths. Understanding of nature as every poet and painter and musician knows is not solely derived from physics, chemistry and mathematics : still less is the appreciation of natural beauty conditional upon this kind of understanding. Moreover, the reference to D'Arcy Thompson is a mere caricature ; the final paragraph of his Huxley lecture flatly contradicts it. " What

---

[1] *D'Arcy Wentworth Thompson*, by Ruth Thompson, 1958, pp. 232-3.

[2] He mentions these beliefs in a very brief and inadequate form, l.c. p. 226, and explaining them admits that physics and chemistry do not include biological problems like heredity or memory or disease : but urges that we piece together such constituent parts as make up the physical-chemical elements in the belief that these when integrated will give us a complete solution. Thompson left room for much more ; Medawar does not.

is it", he asked, "that the physicist and the mathematician and the biologist alike, resting from their labours, see looking out of Mother Nature's eyes? They see dimly what Plato and Pythagoras and Aristotle and Coleridge and Wordsworth saw clearly. . . . You may call it Entelechy ; you may call it the Harmony of the World ; you may call it the *élan vital* ; you may call it the Breath of Life, or you may call it, as it is called in the Story-book of Creation and in the hearts of men, you may call it the spirit of God."[1] Dr. Medawar calls such a claim the superstition that what is beautiful and moving in Nature is in its mystery and its unrevealed designs, and he adds, "D'Arcy did away for all time with this neo-romantic nonsense."[2] Dr. Medawar has misjudged D'Arcy Thompson more favourably than he has done Teilhard : but he is grotesquely mistaken in both cases ; and for the same reason.

For, of course, his basic assumption that science consists solely of physics, chemistry and mathematics, and that only these disciplines provide sound knowledge of nature is a relapse into the crude notion that a world of personal awareness and relationships can be interpreted in terms which leave personality and indeed vast ranges of energy which we apprehend but cannot yet or perhaps ever intellectually comprehend necessarily out of account. To splutter words like nonsense whenever this restriction is ignored is to identify sense with logic ; and anyone who has any fullness of experience knows that this is to equate the whole with one of its parts, the organism with one of its instruments. By all means let our zoologists investigate the components of somatic existence and show us how far as a result of those researches they can interpret the meaning and values, the insights and adventures of life. But when Dr. Medawar tells us that what he does not understand

[1] *The Shell of the Nautilus* (1917). This passage is quoted in the biography of Thompson in which Medawar's verdict appears.

[2] L.c. p. 233. This criticism deserves the epithet which its author applied to Teilhard. It is " self-deceiving "—as everyone who knew D'Arcy will insist.

must be profound, his sneer is truer than he knows : for his knowledge of men—under their skins—is, I fear, definitely subhuman. In any case, it is sad for those of us who have spent half a century in urging that science must soon extend its frontiers and take all intellectual life into its sphere, to see a brilliant zoologist reverting to these outworn limitations and losing his temper and manners with those who cannot accept them.[1]

---

[1] His review of the *Phenomenon* in *Mind*, LXX, pp. 99–106, though called a Critique violates most of the principles of criticism. He starts with a few aphorisms ascribed to Teilhard for which no references or contexts are given, collects a catena of epithets translated in a book of 300 pages, and of neologisms which he never attempts to interpret, cites two short passages describing reproduction and emergence but again without reference or context, and shows no sign of recognizing either that Teilhard is in fact using terms often familiar in French science and philosophy, or that this thought is linked with reputable and profound solutions to problems of universal human interest. He concludes by stating that Teilhard is a " naturalist ", who " practised an intellectually unexacting kind of science " and " achieved a moderate proficiency " ; that he is catering for " the market for works of this kind, for philosophy-fiction ", that he writes " tipsy, euphoric [*sic*] prose-poetry " and that he " can be excused of dishonesty only on the grounds that before deceiving others he has taken great pains to deceive himself ".

In view of the record of Teilhard's life, character and integrity set out in this book, comment on this assault upon him is unnecessary. Its language can hardly be paralleled since the pontifical heresy-huntings of the fifth century. Let me recommend to Dr. Medawar the writings of St. Epiphanius. The high-priests of scientism are following a bad example—but the saint though equally vituperative was a better critic.

Index

INDEX

Alexander, S., 22, 150–1
Alfieri, A., 32
Allard, Baron A., 111–12
Allen, E. L., 24
Andersson, J. G., 79, 124 n.
Andrews, C. W., 56
Andrews, R. C., 83
Aragonnès, C., *see* Mlle M. Teil-lard-Chambon, 11, 43 n.
Archimedes, 20
Ardrey, R., 130–1, 135
Aristotle, 20
Armagnac, C. d', 44–5
Arouet, F. M. (Voltaire), 30
Augustine, St., of Hippo, 161, 207–8

Bacon, Lord F., 18
Bacon, R., 22
Bacot, J., 65–6
Bailly, J. B., 143
Baldwin, J. M., 92
Barbour, G. B., 10, 58 n., 66, 68–9, 80, 81, 83, 103, 107, 111, 124
Barnes, Bishop E. W., 24
Barth, K., 25, 29, 104, 154
Bateson, W., 53, 61, 146
Bégouen, M. H., 43 n., 86 n., 90 n.
Benson, R. H., 62
Berdiaeff, N., 103
Bergson, H., 21, 34, 37–40, 124

Black, P. Davidson, 69, 79, 81, 94
Blondel, M., 10, 40–2, 44–5, 189
Bohlin, B., 124
Borne, E., 155 n.
Bosio, G., 202
Boule, M., 49–51, 56, 65, 124, 135
Brain, Sir W. Russell, 22
Braybrooke, N., 81 n., 140 n., 145 n.
Bréhier, E., 36 n., 44 n.
Breuil, H., 51–2, 61, 63, 66, 98, 123, 126
Broom, R., 39, 104
Bruns, J. E., 208 n.
Buffon, G. L. L. de, 143
Bultmann, R., 13
Burkitt, M., 11, 61, 65, 123

Caius, J., 70–2
Camus, A., 103
Cannon, H. G., 10 n.
Charles, P., 31
Chia, L. P., 81
Clainpanain, J., 32
Clark, D., 108
Clark, Sir W. le Gros, 130
Claudel, P., 83
Cognet, L., 197–202
Collings, H. D., 83
Collingwood, H. G., 20
Combes, E., 35
Corte, N., 37, 49, 202–3

Index

Index